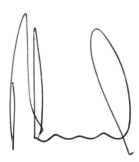

First published in Great Britain in 2014

© Beresford Leavens 2014

All rights reserved; no part of this publication may be reproduced, stored in a
retrieval system, or transmitted in any form or by any means, electronic, mechanical,
photocopying, recording, or otherwise without either the prior written permission of
the Publisher. This book may not be lent, resold, hired out or otherwise disposed of
by way of trade in any form of binding or cover other than that in which it is
published, without the prior consent of the Publisher.

ISBN 978-0-9928482-0-0

Printed and bound in Great Britian by Purely Print, Blandford, Dorset DT11 7TE.
www.purelyprint.co.uk

1

Acknowledgements

I am deeply indebted to the following people, without their help I would have been unable to complete this voyage of discovery into my family history.

A special thanks to my long suffering wife Carol who has put up with this journey of discovery for many years.

My sister, Monica Fulford, & Esther Hicks, Susan Favre, for all their help with the editing of this book.

Peter Rush, of Chettle for the front cover and line drawings.

A very special thanks to the late Mr V. J. Adams of Blandford. We both worked together on this project who very generously gave me much of his research work in the 1970's to help me with a "future project" about my great, great, great, great, grandfather Isaac Gulliver, based on the work by Mr H.V.F. Stone, now held at the Dorchester County Museum. Peter Harvey and the late Mrs Louisa Jane Harvey (nee Harris) his grandmother, her notes for the information regarding the French Revolution, and the Cornish connections between the Harvey & Harris family's with Isaac Gulliver throughout the South Coast.

P.H Smith, Bournemouth, Joan M Pits, & Wyn Watts, Bournemouth, Through a Georgian Window. Roger Guttridge, Dorset Smugglers. The Dorset County Museum, Dorchester, The Bournemouth Evening Echo, The Russell-Coats Museum, Bournemouth. Jeffrey E. Post, Ph.D. Curator National Gem and Mineral Collection Smithsonian Institution. Washington, USA. E.T.C. Bourke, J.P.C. Bourke, P.J.C. Bourke, Mrs Susan Favre, Chettle. Katie Hanks, David Watkins of the Poole History Centre, and Poole Museum Service, Poole. H.V.F. Stone's original memoirs, Bank notes, Mr Blount, by kind permission of David Ashford, copyright of the Dorset Natural History and Archaeological Society at Dorset County Museum, Dorchester. Michael Hodges, Highcliffe. Bonny Sartin poem. The Christchurch Library, Christchurch. Maureen Penrose, Kingston Lacy information. John Spedding, bank notes.

The story, A premature death was passed down through the family to me by my grand mother and mother.

The Family tree of the author Beresford O'Hara Leavens to Isaac Gulliver

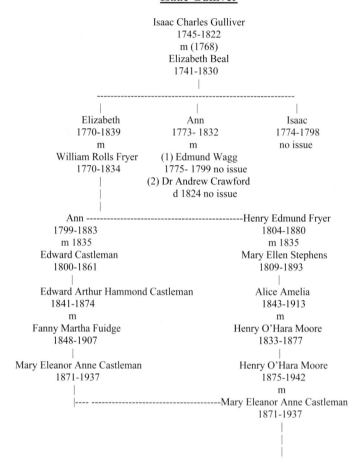

Isaac Charles Gulliver
1745-1822
m (1768)
Elizabeth Beal
1741-1830

|

| | |

Elizabeth	Ann	Isaac
1770-1839	1773- 1832	1774-1798
m	m	no issue
William Rolls Fryer	(1) Edmund Wagg	
1770-1834	1775- 1799 no issue	
	(2) Dr Andrew Crawford	
	d 1824 no issue	

Ann --Henry Edmund Fryer
1799-1883   1804-1880
m 1835   m 1835
Edward Castleman   Mary Ellen Stephens
1800-1861   1809-1893
| |
Edward Arthur Hammond Castleman   Alice Amelia
1841-1874   1843-1913
m   m
Fanny Martha Fuidge   Henry O'Hara Moore
1848-1907   1833-1877
| |
Mary Eleanor Anne Castleman   Henry O'Hara Moore
1871-1937   1875-1942
| m
|---- ------------------------------------Mary Eleanor Anne Castleman
                                                  1871-1937
                                                  |
                                                  |
                                                  |

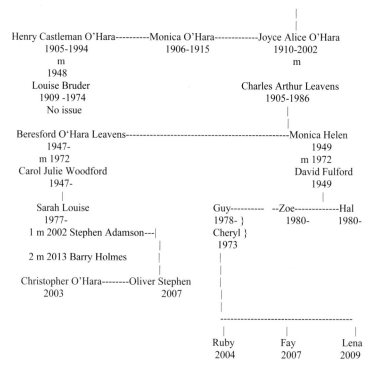

```
                                                    |
                                                    |
Henry Castleman O'Hara----------Monica O'Hara-------------Joyce Alice O'Hara
        1905-1994                  1906-1915               1910-2002
            m                                                  m
          1948
      Louise Bruder                              Charles Arthur Leavens
       1909 -1974                                      1905-1986
        No issue                                          |
                                                          |
Beresford O'Hara Leavens------------------------------------------------Monica Helen
      1947-                                                     1949
     m 1972                                                    m 1972
  Carol Julie Woodford                                      David Fulford
      1947-                                                    1949
        |                                                        |
   Sarah Louise                            Guy----------  --Zoe-------------Hal
      1977-                                1978- }         1980-         1980-
  1 m 2002 Stephen Adamson---|             Cheryl }
                             |             1973
  2 m 2013 Barry Holmes      |              |
                             |              |
  Christopher O'Hara-------Oliver Stephen   |
       2003                  2007           |
                                            |
                                            --------------------------------------
                                            |            |              |
                                          Ruby          Fay           Lena
                                          2004          2007          2009
```

This is a small part of the family tree, I apologise to all those left out
as there is insufficient space to put you all in.

An introduction to the early days of smuggling

Since time immemorial men have found ways to avoid tithes and dues levied on them by their superiors. In an island such as Great Britain imported goods could easily be checked and therefore taxed, so all around the coast smuggling became a way of life to avoid the duties imposed by the Monarchy to help raise money for their armies.

As with all illegal activities, it is impossible to say how many people have been involved in smuggling over the years. Of course it continues to this day, but the type of contraband has changed over time as the taxes imposed on goods have been changed at the whim of the current government.

In the eighteenth century the highest taxes, some as much as two hundred percent were on items such as brandy, spirits, silk, wines and tea. Luxury goods were in short supply from France due to the on going hostilities between the two countries. The demand from those who could afford such luxuries continued driving the smugglers ever harder in their illicit trade. It is well worth remembering that many an aristocratic family would help to finance the boats and their cargoes without it being known that they were involved in any way.

Were the smugglers free traders, organised criminals, villains, or local heroes? We will find out later how local attitudes came to help Isaac Gulliver, a smuggler of some repute who operated from Arundel in the East to the far reaches of Cornwall in the west.

Isaac Gulliver came from Semington in Wiltshire, but lived mainly in the area to the north of what we now know as Bournemouth. During his lifetime this was heath land with only one house on the cliff tops overlooking the sea. His life was spent outwitting the Revenue Officers along the south coast, and none did it better than he. A man of almost giant proportions, towering above his compatriots in more ways than one; he was quick, cunning, determined, wily, devious, and highly intelligent. It's also worth remembering that the sandy beaches between Christchurch and Swanage, now densely populated, were bordered only by heath land which gave unobstructed entry into the countryside, well away from prying eyes.

This land was owned or controlled by members of the extended family into which his daughter married, giving him much freedom to carry out his trade unobstructed by the law.

How fortunate that Old Gulliver's long standing friend and probable partner, Roger Ridout, was his most trusted lieutenant with his brother-in-law William Beale lending support. His army of loyal men, known as 'the White Wigs' changed in numbers depending on the work at hand, but Roger remained by his side and never let down his Old Master.

Modern smugglers still do their best to outwit the customs officers who now have sophisticated machinery to detect the illicit cargos which now consist of humans, drugs, and to a lesser extent, cigarettes, spirits, and other expensive taxable items. The battle of wits continues to this day to defraud the government of taxes due on imported goods. It's no wonder that smuggling has played such a major role in this country's heritage, with stories abounding about many of those who were caught in the past.

The eighteenth century was the heyday of the smuggler: The Hawkhurst gang, Mr Rattenbury, (of Beer, nr Seaton, Devon), The Mayfield Gang, the Adlington Gang, and the Carter family of Prussia Cove were some of the most well known, whilst many more individuals crossed the channel in fishing boats to France or the Channel Islands. Those who were caught were either executed, imprisoned or could enter the navy to fight for the King as a punishment; many chose the latter which was by no means the easy option.

Possibly the most notorious smuggler in the eighteenth century was Isaac Gulliver who was born in Semington, Wiltshire, in 1745. He first came to notice at the age of twelve as a smugglers' assistant, and again in 1763 when he was reputed to be supplying markets as far afield as Warwick, Worcester, Oxford, Bristol and Salisbury. It was reported that at this time he was depriving the Revenue Authorities of some £20,000 per year which would nowadays equate to about £1,600,000 much in line with the larger drug barons of today.

Gulliver was a man of many parts; landlord, horse dealer, property owner; he owned several ships, and during his heyday supplied the money which helped to create The Wimborne Blandford and Christchurch Bank in Wimborne which in turn partially funded the creation of Bournemouth town as we know it today. He was also involved in assisting the aristocracy flee France during the French Revolution, which made him popular with aristos on both sides of the Channel.

Some parts of this book must be viewed with a pinch of salt, most are based on facts given to the author or passed down through his family. However, not every story can be guaranteed to be 100% authenticated as many were passed by word of mouth and some written many years later, with possibly a little writers' license – but we can be assured that truth is stranger than fiction, and the many legends and stories that surround this larger than life character, are probably not far from accurate.

ISSAC GULLIVER. by Bonny Sartin

My name is Gulliver, I'm a smuggler
A smuggler of fame and renown,
I supplies all the liquor
From Christchurch to Dorchester town.
My business is imports and imports
I'm an important man in these parts,
I delivers the liquid refreshments
That warms up the coldest of hearts.
The gentry likes fine wines and brandy
Others they likes tots of rum,
So when they are planning a party
It's to Isaac Gulliver they come.
The magistrates treat me quite gently
'Cos anything their cellar lacks,
They know they can buy from me cheaply
At fifty per cent minus tax.
I've a band of good men that work for me
A loyal and trustworthy crew,
They deal with the customs and excise
Don't cross them or they'll deal with you

Gulliver –The beginning

Leading the captured horses away

In the moonlight which shone fitfully between the flying clouds, Isaac raised his head cautiously to scan his surroundings. At 12 years of age, he was already almost as tall as his father, with promise of a strong frame once the gangliness of youth had passed. He was tired of the hand to mouth existence of his father's village inn, with its never ending mind numbing chores; serving ale to drunken labourers, and cleaning up after them, everything smelling of fermented beer and unwashed bodies. He preferred mucking out the stables for the coaching horses, tending to his mother's scrawny chickens, and selling their few eggs and vegetables at the local market. He could already read, write and count far better than his father and contemporaries and yearned for a better life.

So, having listened carefully to his father's comments and those of his customers, he had gleaned enough information to know with some certainty that tonight there would be a cargo arriving on the tide, to be transported inland to a secret cache not that far away.

His intention was to follow and at some stage, make his presence known and ask to be included in the next run.

Straining his ears to catch the first signs of approaching horses over the sound of the wind, he waited. At last his patience was rewarded. He felt the vibration of hoof beats, then murmuring voices and jangling bits, faintly at first but coming steadily closer. He lay still in the heather, determined to wait until they had passed so he could follow undetected. His stomach churned with excitement as they passed oblivious to his hiding place.

He was about to rise when shouts and clash of steel signalled a raid by the Revenue men. Shots were fired, screams, moans and grunts pinpointed the position of the fight, right at the edge of some trees. Isaac crept around the battle to find the string of ponies had halted and were unattended. Adrenalin surging, he laid hold of the lead bridle and quietly led the animals off the track, deep into the woods. Thinking as they went, he tethered the pony to a tree while he carefully obliterated their tracks, then continued to lead his little cavalcade by a circuitous route to a barn his father owned on the edge of their village.

Knowing his father had connections with smugglers and did a little himself he thought it would be safe to take the animals home. Inside the ramshackle wooden building he made the sturdy ponies comfortable and relieved them of their burdens which he hid behind bales of straw and old sacks, promising himself to investigate their contents in daylight. He then stole back in to the house and shook his father awake, knowing he would have to explain the presence of three extra animals before they were simply found in the morning.

"How are we going to feed three extra mouths? You'd best turn them loose for someone else to bother with." his father said.

"I'll find a way to pay for their food." Isaac said. "At the least, I can take them to market and sell them."

"Their owners will recognize them and turn you over to the Authorities." father grumbled.

"Not if I take them into Hampshire markets, away from here." the boy replied. "They're mine. I found 'em and I shall use them to make money for us all, so don't you go telling anyone or turning them away."

Isaac's face loomed menacingly over his father in the dark, so that his father just grunted as he turned over to go back to sleep.

"You're getting too big for your boots, my lad, find out who owned them or I will."

As Isaac completed his chores the next morning, he was formulating his plans. The ponies, gentle, strong creatures, probably from the New Forest, whickered as he entered the barn. They stood patiently as he fed and watered them, and cleaned around their hooves. His next task was to inspect the hidden bundles. His hands were shaking as he unwrapped bolts of silk, packets of spices, and counted the casks of brandy. In one satchel were several coins, carefully wrapped in a leather pouch and in another were papers with lists of customers for the contraband. His heart leapt with joy - he knew where to sell these items.

But Isaac was an intelligent lad and he quickly realised he couldn't just approach these wealthy merchants and landowners direct. To start with, they would not deal with a simple Innkeepers boy; secondly they would inform the smugglers who had stolen the cargo and retribution would quickly follow. His family would be beaten, the Inn burnt to the ground, and they would be destitute. He would have to be cunning and patient. It was time to take his fathers advice and find those that had lost their animals and contraband.

The next Saturday he harnessed their old cob and drove his mother to market with her eggs and a few vegetables to sell. He wandered around listening carefully to every conversation he could. Then he visited the taverns where he looked for signs of recent fighting on the men's faces. In a secluded corner he found two bruised men hunched forwards talking to the Squire's man of business.

"We was lucky." one of them was saying. "Jeremy and two others was taken and are in jail, but we managed to escape and hide until they'd gone. But they soldiers must have taken the ponies and the cargo cos there weren't no sign of them when we went back. The Revenue have put up posters saying anyone who finds the goods must hand it in, but we reckon the officer has kept it for himself."

"As you know, the Squire has already paid for the silk and spices - it was for his daughters wedding - so it will go bad for you if he finds you are keeping it for yourselves." the other replied.

"Oh, no sir, no sir, we wouldn't do that. Squire is a good man and a reliable customer. We wouldn't steal from the likes of him.

"Tis risky enough without upsetting such as him."

Isaac had heard enough and carefully crept away. So, the Revenue men thought the smugglers had retrieved their goods, and the smugglers thought the Revenue had stolen it. All well and good but it meant he couldn't sell to any one named on the list. Sitting outside he was silent, forming his plan. If I tell these men that I managed to capture the goods and ponies perhaps they will let me join them.

Young Gulliver waited until the men appeared. Walking up to them he said he wanted a word in private.

"Why would we want to talk to a young scruff like you?"

"Cos I have information that will interest you, I knows where your ponies and the goods are."

"Then tell us boy, and make it quick."

It wasn't long before the animals and goods were spirited away and a couple of gold coins were given to the young lad. Now he had an opening into the smugglers ring.

Being just a lad, he was able to listen out for any mention of smuggling, the revenue men, fishing boats, tides and weather. In this way he gathered enough information to make an intelligent guess of when and where the next illicit cargo would be landed. He also ran errands for the Revenue, feeding them false information while gaining their trust. Thus he was able to warn the smugglers that the Revenue would be waiting for them at the same place as the last ambush.

The smuggler grabbed Isaac roughly and dragged him to the 'boss'.

"How'd you know all this? Who are you, I've a good mind to throw you into the sea and let you drown."

"I can help you. I've been listening at the Customs House and I know how you can give them the slip." Isaac wasn't frightened of their bluster.

"I know you have to land the cargo at high tide, but instead of taking it inland straight away, you need to find somewhere different to store it for a few days. Then when the soldiers have given up, split it up into separate loads so if one is taken, the others get through. I can help; I know where you can store things until the coast is clear."

In this way Isaac became a trusted member of the gang, and with his intelligence and business acumen, to say nothing of his increasing size and belligerence, moved up the chain of command until he became the leader of a highly organised company of smugglers with contacts all over the south coast.

The preserve of Isaac Gulliver stretched from Pevensey Castle in Sussex to the far reaches of Cornwall. Owned by nobility and the gentry, this land had been passed down through generations since William the Conqueror, when he had distributed it as reward to loyal followers.

The families of such landed gentry were related to each other through marriage and their domains covered much of southern England, and remained so through the centuries. This then was Isaac Gulliver's territory. He came to know these aristocratic families well and was accepted and trusted by them in his later life.

The start

Salisbury Crown Court

Born in Semington, Wiltshire, in 1745 to mother
Elizabeth and father Isaac Gulliver, nothing is known of
him until he was 12 when our attention is drawn to his
first recorded connection with smugglers where he was
described as a "smugglers' assistant" at Salisbury Crown
Court. After this, his first brush with the law, his name
doesn't appear again in any court records during his
lifetime, only those of the Revenue from time to time
throughout his long and prosperous career.

It is possible that his father was a regular customer of a
small group of men with seafaring connections, as he
was the landlord of a local Inn, he may have lent a hand
from time to time. Most likely this is how he was
introduced to smuggling and his father gave him into the
care of a lad named Roger, some 9 years older than
Isaac, telling him to keep an eye on the boy.
This lad was Roger Ridout and the two quickly formed
a lifelong bond. As Isaac Gulliver entered his teens

Roger discovered that the boy's brain was quick, calculating, and successful, rarely making incorrect decisions. As time passed they left Isaac's father and his small group of smugglers and set up on their own. Isaac was by now in charge as, recognising that Gulliver was the natural leader, Roger became his trusted right hand man. This worked well as Roger had many contacts and was able to bring landsmen into this newly formed young gang.

Isaac Gulliver lived mostly in the Dorset region, but when things became too hot, with the Revenue close on his heels, he moved west to Devon or Cornwall, or headed east to Sussex, where he could continue his trade away from the prying eyes of the local Revenue officers in the Christchurch, Poole and the Weymouth area.

In 1762 several Revenue Officers were holding a man they thought was a smuggler. They offered him a deal. He was to lead them to a cargo of smuggled goods. If the Revenue officers succeeded in capturing and detaining the smugglers and their cargo, he would be paid for every cask of spirits and hundredweight of tea that was seized. The deal was struck, and the hapless Joseph Manuel duly did the deed some weeks later.

Revenue officers confiscated the illicit cargo and took it to the Poole Customs House for safe storage. The Poole Collector of Customs then reneged on the deal by reducing the amount paid to Joseph Manuel. Manuel found himself an attorney who fought his case, and won! Unfortunately for Joseph Manual, bringing this arrangement to court meant the local gang of smugglers found out about it. They broke into his house in Christchurch, and beat him severely.

They then slung him over the back of a horse, head to one side, and feet on the other, tied to his hands under the belly of the animal, and carried him across Bourn Heath to Bourn House, an isolated building currently frequented by Isaac Gulliver and his smugglers. He was held there until they could transport him to the Channel Islands where he was abandoned in a sorry state.

When he finally managed to escape and make his way back to Christchurch he reported the story of his capture and transportation to the Commissioner of Customs, who in turn offered a reward of '£50 for information leading to the conviction of those responsible.'

The reward was never claimed. One can only surmise that if Isaac Gulliver, aged 17, was involved in this incident, then his powerful control over the area was already taking effect on the local inhabitants.

It is fair to say that the smugglers worked in well run and strongly united gangs, often sponsored by those in authority with money to invest. Isaac Gulliver quickly became the acknowledged leader of these gangs; his intelligence and organizational skills welding the disparate groups of smugglers into one unit. Anyone breaking ranks was swiftly and severely dealt with. Loyalty and discretion were of the utmost importance as this illegal trade paid more than could be earned honestly on land or at sea fishing. Ten shillings a week was the average wage, but a 'tubs' man could earn that in a night, far more even than a Riding Officer, or a Dragoon.

In 1768, when Isaac was 23 years old, he had grown into a tall, powerfully built young man, standing a good head above the average man of the time. His career as a full time smuggler was well under way, his connections growing, but more importantly his quick cunning and agile mind was his saviour. Due to the hardships endured by landsmen and other locals who mostly lived on the breadline, he was held in respect by the local community, and Roger Ridout, his eyes and ears, was constantly at his side. It is well worth noting that Gulliver's men never carried pistols (only Gulliver did).

They carried coshes made from wood, and Blackjacks, lead covered woven rope coshes about two feet long, which, if you were hit by one on your head, would put you out for the count.

Ships were organized with regular arrivals along the Bourne coastal region. Occasional scuffles broke out with the Revenue officers if they chanced upon some booty, but on the whole there was little trouble as the smugglers far outnumbered the handful of officers stationed in Christchurch and Poole.

The area between Poole and Christchurch was open heath; land covered in gorse and scrub with dense areas of pine trees with few paths or tracks, which afforded the very best of cover and superb hiding places for the vast quantities of smuggled goods. Once on land the duty free contraband was transported away from the coast by different routes as quickly as was possible, even deep into the far flung regions of central England.

In many instances instead of sailing vessels, the crafty smugglers used long boats with eight oars which could out smart and out run the revenue cutters by rowing directly into wind once they had seen a Revenue cutter.

These long boats could keep up a steady nine knots; they were designed to be seaworthy and fast, and could cross the channel in a single night. By contrast, the revenue cutters were unable to sail directly into the wind and had to tack, forcing them to cover a much greater distance than the long boats which could travel in a straight line independent of the wind. Long boats were hardly ever caught by a revenue cutter unless one came upon the smugglers by chance and was able to corner it against the beach.

The frustration the Revenue Officers felt is quite understandable, as they asked on more than one occasion to have their boats built by the same shipyards that built the smugglers vessels and to the same design. Some were between two and three hundred tonnes and carried up to 24 guns. These ships were not to be trifled with as the smugglers were determined people and would not surrender.

They had no reason to surrender; if caught, the possible sentence could be "the long drop." Alternatively, they could be conscripted into the Navy, and forced to fight for King and country.

Life on board these ships was cruel for the convicted. They were worked extra hard and never allowed ashore when in harbour. The King's ships were frequently at sea for years at a time, leaving the convicts' families without a bread winner, often starving and having to enter the work house. Life for the majority was already hand to mouth and the families of anyone caught smuggling was particularly hard. The revenue knew that if they were cornered either on land or sea, the smugglers would put up a fierce fight as they had little to lose.

The following report from the Cowes Customs House gives an idea of the battle over smuggled goods that took place in those days between both sides. There is no evidence Gulliver was involved in this battle with the Revenue.

To:
Custom House, London.
From: Customs House, Cowes.
No. 88.   20th July 1784.
Hon. Sirs,
On the 16th inst. Two large Lugsail vessels were brought into this Port by the Officers of the "Orestes" Sloop of War having been seized in Christchurch Harbour by them, in conjunction with Mr James Sarmon Commander of an Excise Revenue Cutter and Mr. George Sarmon Commander of the "Swan" Cutter in the service at this Port for having the proceeding day unlawfully imported and run a large quantity of tea and foreign spirits near Christchurch Head within the limits of the Port of Southampton.

We are sorry to acquaint your Honours that the Officers were oppos'd, obstructed and wantonly fired upon when rowing into Christchurch Harbour and before they had landed or taken possession of the vessels by a number of smugglers assembled onboard the Lugger and on the shore. Mr. Allen, Master of the "Orestes" and who also acted under a Deputation from your Honours was shot and is since dead and one of the Mariners wounded in the arm. An inquest has been taken on the body of Mr.

Allen. The jury having returned a verdict of Wilful Murder, the Coroner had issued warrants for apprehending William Parrott and William May, two persons who were proved to have been accessaries in the Murder; none of the rest are yet known or discovered. A transaction of this kind having happened in the face of day, and so near Christchurch it is more than probable that many of the persons assembled on the spot must be known in that neighbourhood especially as the smugglers sheltered themselves in a Public House called the Haven House, from the windows of which, and the stable adjoining, several muskets were fired at the Officers.

We have judged it necessary to write to Mr. Jeans, Supervisor of the Riding Officers at Christchurch, to excite him to use his endeavours to apprehend the offenders and to transmit any information he may collect that is likely to lead to a discovery of any of Persons concerned in the Murder.

Never was a more unprovoked attack made on Officers of the Revenue than in the present instance and it shows how necessary exemplary punishment is for such daring violators of the Law.

The smugglers had not even the pretence to urge of firing in their own defence, for many shots were fired on the Officers from behind sand banks and sheltered places and Mr. Allen who was first wounded in the thigh and afterwards in the body received his death wound before a single gun was fired by the Revenue Officers.

A report having gone abroad that before the intended Act for preventing of smuggling takes place, an Act of oblivion for all smuggling offences will also be passed, we are fully persuaded they are induced to act in a more daring and desperate manner under an idea (but a mistaken one we hope) that all offences against the Revenue or outrages on Officers will be pardoned.

From the very great numbers concerned (as the Officers report) in this business, we are humbly of opinion that if Pardon and a reward was offered to any of the persons so unlawfully assembled except those who actually fired or killed the Officer, it might lead to arrest of the most atrocious offenders.

Inclosed we transmit to you two lists found on board one of the vessels, they contain the names of many persons known to be noted smugglers. The Officers were repeatedly fired upon from persons on board the vessels, tho they all quitted scuttled and carried away the sails before the officers could get up to the beach, where they were run on shore. It is but reasonable to suppose the persons belonged to them were some of those concerned.

We submit to your honours whether it will not be sufficient for advertising and apprehending them on suspicion. At any rate we hope your Honours will order such steps to be taken as you may think most likely to bring the offenders to Justice.

The Vessels under seizure were seen the proceeding day employed in landing a very large quantity of tea and foreign spirits which were carried off between two and three o'clock in the afternoon by upwards of 50 waggons and two or three hundred horses, but the smugglers would not suffer W Sarmon of the Excise Cutter who fell in with them at the time either to go on board the vessels or take away any of the goods which were on the shore.

*He stood to sea again and meeting with the "Orestes"
and "Swan" Cutters they joined and went in pursuit of
the vessels which they seized as before mentioned.
We are Etc. W, Arnold. 1. R.*

An advertisment for the sale of conviscated goods to be
sold at the Custom House, Poole. 1784.

POOLE, DORSET.

ON Monday the 29th day of March, 1784, at three
o'clock in the afternoon, will be expofed to public Sale,
at the Cuftom-houfe in this port,

For HOME CONSUMPTION.

Brandy, in large calks,	—	2201	Gallons.
Rum,	—	41	
Geneva, in large cafks,	—	1009	
French Wine,	—	10	
Oporto Wine, in bottles,	—	20	Dozen.
Lifbon Wine, ditto,	—	20	
Coals,	—	31	Chaldrons.
Raw Coffee,	—	66	Pounds.
Nankeen,	—	1	Piece.

All which goods have been feized and condemned, and may
be viewed at any time, in his Majefty's warehoufe at that port,
(in proper hours) two days before the fale.

The Blacksmiths Arms

The Blacksmith's Arms of Thorney Down, Woodcuts,
Dorset was owned by Mr William Cross of Blandford
and tenanted by Mr William Beale. Gulliver supplied
the Blacksmith's Arms with spirits, and wines, making a
good return himself on his investment.

Was it here that he first met his future wife? Daughter
of William Beale. Elizabeth was his lifelong soul mate,

accepting and understanding his roguish ways which were to bring them a fortune in later life; a fortune so great it would help fund the town of Bournemouth some 50 years later. They married in 1768 at the Parish Church of St. Mary the Virgin, Sixpenny Handley, in the presence of Nathanial Bestland and Thomas Beach. Normally one of the witnesses would be the bride's father. Although the clerk has entered the name Beale, the bride's signature is illegible. Could she have been writing under some sort of duress which made a mess of the signature?

In many ways this marriage throws up more questions than it answers. According to Chettle records, Elizabeth's father, William Beale, lived at St Marys Farm House, Chettle, he was also landlord of the Blacksmith's Arms at Thorney Down, in the parish of Woodcuts, just a few miles away. He was a person of some importance in the local community. He farmed in Chettle he also kept the Poor Book, he was also the right hand man of George Chafin JP, the Lord of the Manor. This was a man running with the deer and hunting with the hounds.

Why did Elizabeth marry in the Parish Church of St. Mary the Virgin, Sixpenny Handley, and not at St Mary's Church, Chettle? That would have been the normal place to hold her wedding. Why was the marriage by licence? Normally marriage banns would have been read over three weeks, as marriages by licence were expensive and out of the reach of most people, only chosen if the marriage was urgent for some reason.

Their first born was some two years after the marriage so it is unlikely that she was pregnant.

Possibly Isaac and Elizabeth eloped to get married. It has been suggested from stories passed down through the family that William Beale of Chettle was most definitely not in favour of his daughter's marriage to Isaac, or at least he had to make the case as he was also working for or with George Chafin JP. We know that Gulliver was in court at the age of 12, charged with being a 'smugglers' assistant. From that time forward he was involved in the crime of smuggling, and therefore in the handling of stolen goods. What self respecting person would want a son-in-law with those credentials? It is therefore understandable that her father William Beale, a personage of some importance, would avoid the wedding at all costs; hence no signature on the wedding certificate and the shaky hand of Elizabeth as can be seen on the document. No doubt in private he was extremely happy about the marriage as its certain that they were in partnership in their illicit trade.

Isaac and Elizabeth Gulliver had three children; Elizabeth born in 1770, Ann 1773, and Isaac his son in 1774; all were born at the Blacksmith's Arms where he was now living. Isaac had a great affinity with Chettle and the surrounding area. Not only his wife Elizabeth came from here, he also rented Thickthorn Farm, a mere mile away from Chettle, and a short distance from the Sturts of Long Crichel who were involved at one time in the transportation of illicit cargos across the Channel.

They owned several ships carrying coal, chalk, limestone, and manure, which sailed around the coast transporting these cargoes to wherever they were required. Why manure should be transported to Poole or

Brownsea Island is not recorded. Possibly it was a way of camouflaging casks of spirits at times.

Newspaper cuttings:

'In 1897 a 'Smuggler's Hole' was discovered at Wimborne St Giles, Referring to this, the Dorset County Chronicle of October 14, 1891 said An interesting relic of smuggling has been discovered on the Chalbury farm of the Earl of Shaftesbury's St Giles Estate. This is one of the genuine 'East Holes' in which contraband of note were concealed in the course of their transit from the coast between Lytchett, Poole, and Christchurch to the inland towns. The discovery was made while ploughing some land, when the horse, which was a young and valuable one, suddenly fell into a large hollow, from which the carter succeeded in extricating it without injury Examination then showed a small cellar about five feet deep, cut in the solid chalk of the sub soil it was shaped like a beehive, the diameter was about five feet at the base, and a side entrance to it could be traced. A generation or two back state that this portion of the property consisted of small copses and patches of woodland which would afford cover to the smugglers, and there is abundant evidence that the villagers of this district were ready accomplices, prepared for a 'run' when the 'goods' had been landed.'

In 1983 some cattle escaped onto the back lawn of Chettle House, one unfortunate animal fell through the lawn into an underground hole. Having removed the beast the hole was examined and found to be exactly the same as that found at Wimborne St Giles, a genuine 'East Hole.' Once again giving credence to the illegal activities taking place on the Lord of the Manor's lawn, George Chafin JP.

Chettle House, 'East Hole' off to the bottom right
of the lawn

'An old Dorset agriculturist told the writer a few years ago that he remembered a lad about 1823 that said one of his father's labourers came into the house one morning with the news that a straw rick had been pulled about during the night. A careful search explained the cause some smugglers being hard pressed had turned into the field where a rick was situated and had carefully hidden a number of kegs of spirits, covering the rick up carefully again. The next night, the Preventive officers having given up the pursuit, the smugglers returned for their goods which they carried away, but this time did not take the trouble to replace the straw hence the labourer's discovery.'

In about 1772 when Isaac Gulliver was 27 years old, the Poole Collector of Revenue wrote that after conducting a lengthy inquiry into the state of smuggling locally: "We find that Isaac Gulliver, William Beale, (Blacksmith's Arms) and Roger Ridout run great quantities of goods on our North Shore between Poole and Christchurch." It is not possible to say what 'great quantities' amount to, but it's fair to say that there were several ships a week, and possibly nightly landings especially in the winter months with their longer dark nights.

Round about this time the Local Revenue officers realised that with the small number of men under their command it would be extremely difficult to apprehend the local smugglers red handed. Instead, everything possible was done by means of offering rewards of money and free pardons to gain information which would lead to the conviction of any smugglers.

By 1778 William Beale was no longer landlord of the King's Arms (previously known as The Blacksmith Arms).

An Advertisement in the Salisbury & Winchester Journal, June 1, 1778 announced the sale of all stock, which comprised:

'30 horses, 15 beasts, 100 sheep, household goods, china, etc: also two hogshead of good brandy and rum: also the remainder of the lease, of which 7 years were unexpired, also hay and corn and hay on the ground.'

By early 1779, the Inn had a new name and new tenant:
'The Thorney Down Inn is now kept by George Moore at, Thorney Down aforesaid near Blandford, where all

Gentlemen who shall please to honour him with their company may depend on his utmost endeavours to please.
Gentlemen on journeys may be accommodated also with genteel Post- Chaises, careful drivers, and exceeding good horses.'

The Thorney Down Inn was well placed on the main road from Blandford to Salisbury. It was a small drinking Inn and well able to handle the local people wanting a post chase. The main coaching stop, several miles down the road at Thickthorn also had a bar for refreshments and food. This was where the teams of horses were changed on the long coach journey to and from London, Salisbury, Blandford, Dorchester and Weymouth. The approaching coach drivers would blow their horns giving warning of their arrival as they broached the hill on either side of the coaching stop about a mile distant, warning the stable lads of their imminent arrival, allowing them time to harness the horses and have the new team ready and waiting to replace the blown animals.

The changeover would only take a few minutes, and the tired beasts would then be fed and watered. Later they would replace the team on another coach during the day or they might be fortunate enough to have a rest in the field next door before being harnessed up the following day. Isaac Gulliver had a large barn useful for storage close by at Thorny Down, and these establishments were of paramount importance for his business. Being able to travel to London from Weymouth quickly was important in those days, and it was a necessary alibi for Gulliver to own horses that could be used both as pack animals to transport smuggled goods far inland and animals that were trained to work as a team pulling coaches.

The notorious Gulliver

By 1777 Isaac had become well known throughout much of the South Coast and middle England. He had become a man who was respected by those he dealt with, known for his trustworthiness and fairness. Unfortunately, this sentiment did not extend to Levi Payne, who *'absconded from his master Isaac Gulliver of Thorney Down, in the county of Dorset, and took with him £21-16s in money, which he had received on his said master's account, and a bright grey Nag about ten years old.'*

In those days £21-16s was at least half a year's wages for a Revenue Officer. The bright grey nag would have been in good condition and worth a fair amount of money on its own, plus it was obviously harnessed as he rode off on the beast. Had the law caught Levi Payne he would have come before the JP in Blandford, one George Chafin of Chettle, a man who would not tolerate the theft of a sheep let alone a horse. As for the £21-16s from his friend Gulliver one can only speculate what sentence may have been forthcoming. He would either have been hanged or sent to Australia by convict ship, not a pleasant 6 months voyage at all.

There are no records of his capture so one has to assume he never came to trial. We can only speculate that with Gulliver's contacts throughout the country amongst both the Nobility and the Inn keepers in even the smallest far flung villages who relied on his trade to buy illicit wines and spirits, news of Levi Payne's theft of money and a horse would spread like wildfire across the south. Talk in the Taverns and Inns would have been about the possible fate of Levi Payne at Gulliver's hands once caught; he might be strung up from the yard arm of one of his ships, then dropped into the sea, or quietly dropped into a well. As the drink flowed the stories would have become more gruesome but mixed with the drunken laughter would be the knowledge that they wouldn't take the chance to steal from Isaac Gulliver.

A 'handsome reward' would be most welcome from a man they all respected and could possibly lead to even better deals in the future if only they could find the wretch.

Gulliver would have offered a reward in excess of the value of the stolen money and horse put together. To Isaac, a man who had thumbed his nose at the law all his life, this was a trifling incident, but he would ensure his rough justice be done. There is no doubt he would have handed out swift tough punishment when the poor unfortunate Levi Payne was finally bought before him. Possibly he would have been handed to the Crown as a 'willing seaman' having first been forced to work to pay back the value of his theft. Gulliver would need to show those who worked for him, and who might try to take advantage of him, that he could uphold 'his' law and was not to be trifled with. Most assuredly there was no safe hiding place for Levi Payne in the land ruled by King George III.

By 1778 Gulliver was already clearing the decks by buying his pardon through a programme for volunteers, as advertised in the Salisbury & Winchester Journal of June 1, 1778.

VOLUNTEERS. Notice is hereby given to all young and Able Men who are willing to serve his Majesty either by SEA or LAND, that they are wanted to enter immediately and each man approved of will receive a Bounty of TEN GUINEAS, and FIVE GUINEAS to drink his Majesty's health. Apply at Thorney Down, lying on the western road between Salisbury and Blandford. GOD save the KING.

Gulliver hoped that the Commissioners of Customs in London would get to hear that he had bought a pardon. In reality it made him look like an upright and honest citizen for the first time in his life, but as we shall see he had far better connections to keep the law at arm's length, and as for giving up such a highly profitable career; well, that was highly unlikely!

St Andrews Church Kinson

St Andrews Church, Kinson is some 800 years older than Bournemouth, standing on the far side of Bourn Heath, it made a good landmark from the coast with many well worn tracks leading to it.

This was used as a place of storage by the smugglers in the 18th century. There is much evidence of this by the grooves cut into the outside of the castellation's on the tower, If you enter the church you will find more well worn groves in the stone arch at the base of the tower.

Ropes would lead from the ground over the castellations down through the old Norman tower into the central aisle where a group of smugglers would assemble to heave on the ropes. Being seamen they would have a block and tackle rigged up to make the raising of heavy loads quick and simple. In only a few minutes they could have made their contraband secure in the tower ready for later distribution.

There are two interesting graves in the church yard.

The first is to one Robert Trotman, late of Rond in the county Wilts who was barbarously murdered on the shore near Poole the 24th March 1795.

St. Andrew's Church, Kinson

Followed by the inscription:

"A little tea one leaf I did not steal,
For guiltless blood shed I to God appeal
Put tea in one scale human blood in tother
And think what tis to slay thy harmless brother."

There is no evidence that Gulliver was involved in this tragedy, and the court case that followed made no mention of his name. One thing to be remembered is that none of his men went out armed with anything other than 'black jacks,' or clubs, none but Gulliver carried a pistol, the reason, he was determined to protect 'his' men from being charged with murder. Even he couldn't save them from the gallows for such a crime.

There is another interesting tomb in the church and situated to the rear of the church. I'm told in my grandmother's jottings (M. E. A. O'Hara Moore. Nee Castleman) that in the past this tomb had a passageway that ran to the river. The story went that Gulliver was once buried in this grave as we will find out later.

Not far from Kinson lies Hillams Land Farm, a property that's now on Dudsbury Golf Course and owned by the Golf Club, this was in the possession of Isaac Gulliver in 1782. Well hidden under the property is an extremely large cellar well able to hold large quantities of wine and spirits. There would appear to be a bricked up tunnel running from the cellar towards the river a short distance away. William Lockyer, aged 15, went into service and lived for two years as a yearly servant to Gulliver at Hillams Land Farm.

Gulliver and the nobility

Gulliver's contacts among the nobility included 'the Lady Dowager Arundel', who, in 1777, held mortgages for land deeded to Isaac Gulliver. In the original deed Gulliver is described as a yeoman, which was a definite move up the ladder for him.

By the time Gulliver was 33 years old, he was well on his way to owning his property empire. He held tenancies and owned a variety of properties. Most of these properties were ideal for the storage of wines and spirits, very often situated so they would appear to be legitimate in his Inns and wine shop in Devon.

In 1792-3, 'the Lady Dowager Arundel' or her Stewards put their earlier connection to Isaac Gulliver to good use - to the benefit of both parties. It was during this time that Gulliver became intertwined with the Arundels, Howards, Harris, and Harveys, like bindweed growing up a rose bush. These powerful families were large landowners along the South coast who went as far back as William the Conqueror when they were given their lands and titles. In Dorset they were also JPs at Chideock, and Shaftesbury, in Wiltshire the Arundels owned Wardour Castle. Their lands extended throughout Devon and into Cornwall where the Harris's were involved in Privateering in Elizabethan times as well as holding the Stewardship over much of Cornwall.

In order to understand how people lived at that time, it is important to appreciate how the law operated before the advent of Robert Peel and his 'Peelers.'

Large landowners paid 'Stewards' who oversaw their estates which covered vast areas of land. A mere handful of landowners might own a whole county between them. The regulations are laid out below in 'Old English' and show how it was possible for Isaac Gulliver to have the freedom to continue his smuggling activities with those who held power in the region turning a blind eye, and offering little or no hindrance.

It is obvious that they were all involved in one way or another, using Gulliver for their own ends, and protecting him whilst incidentally making him rich. We must also remember that even though these important aristocratic families didn't initially have great sums of money, they were land rich, and by the time Gulliver died they were all extremely wealthy.

Chief Constables had considerable powers. Because they were appointed annually by the Stewards (except such as are particularly specified,) at the different Court Leets, no account of them can be accurately given. A Chief Constable might reside one year in the easternmost part of the county, and the following year could be found presiding in the extreme westernmost part. This migration of officials often led to miscarriages of justice.

In 1792 an attempt was made to remedy this situation charging the Under Sheriff, Town Clerks, and Stewards of the several Courts, within this County, where such High Constables are elected, to prevent, as far as lies in their power, the appointment of persons who are improper, and not responsible, to execute the said office; and also that they, and the acting Magistrates of this County, will reject all such persons who are improper, and not responsible who shall be offered as Deputies; and it is requested, that the Under Sheriff, Town Clerks, and Stewards aforesaid will, within a few days after the election of such Constables or Deputies, at the Courts aforesaid, transmit the names and places of abode of such as shall have been so elected, to the Clerk of the Peace of the said County.

Like the position of chief constable, other major appointments were also made annually. These included the surveyors of highways (annually appointed by the Justices), and overseers of the poor (also appointed by the justices), There was considerable 'nepotism' in many higher appointments. For example, Lord Salisbury's 'Steward for the Hundred' was Mr Edward Hooper who was also the Chairman of the Customs for the local area, living at Heron Court, Nr Christchurch.

His daughter married a Harris who later became the Earl of Malmesbury around 1799.

The Hoopers originally came from Boveridge House, Boveridge, Wimborne.

Mr Bankes of Kingston Lacy, Wimborne, who had five 'hundreds' covering the area joining Lord Salisbury's estates to the north and east, and stretching as far as Corfe Castle, Swanage, and Lulworth. Mr William Castleman (solicitor and banker) was the Steward for Mr Bankes, also the High Constable, with the power to appoint five constables, one for each 'hundred.'

The Hundreds were Bradbury, Cogdean, Hasilor, Rowbarrow, and the Borough of Corfe Castle. The Bailiffs of the Hundreds were appointed through the Court Leets, but if none were appointed the Chief Constables did the duty. The officers collected fines, summoned Juries, and attended the Judges and Justices at the assizes and quarter sessions. The Special Bailiffs executed writs, made arrests and oversaw executions, and were bound to the High Sheriff for due execution of their office.

Two of the Bankes 'Hundreds' were the 'Rowbarrow Hundred' consisting of Whitecliff, Studland, Langton

Matravers, and Worth Matravers. The second was the 'Codgean Hundred' consisting of Parkstone, Hamworthy, Lytchett Minster, Lytchett Matravers and Kingston. These were all coastal areas running down to the sea.

The Marquis of Anglesey had a Hundred called Handley; William Castleman was also the Steward and High Constable of this estate.

The Castlemans acted as Stewards for several estates for over a 100 years; William Castleman (1714-1792) was appointed 'Agent' of the Anglesey estate when he was 55 years old, later it became the Paget Estate. His son William (1766-1844) took over as 'Agent' to the Paget estate on his father's death followed by his son Henry Castleman. The coastal areas controlled by William Castleman as Steward to the Bankes estates were considerable, stretching from the Bourne valley to Lulworth Cove, and with the Hoopers (via his marriage into the Harris family) to the East and much of Sussex.

William Castleman grew to be of great importance to Isaac Gulliver.

Not only was he Gulliver's solicitor and banker, but they were also 'family' by marriage through Gulliver's granddaughter Ann.

Gulliver was extremely well protected from the law through his daughter Elizabeth's marriage into the Fryer family. Isaac Gulliver and the Fryers of Kinson were both much engaged in the smuggling trade over the years, creating a track from Branksome Chine to Kinson through Talbot Woods via 'Pug's Hole.'

The Gullivers lived in an old mud walled house (cobb house with a thatched roof that overlapped the walls by about 18" to keep the rain off the walls, these houses were made of mud, straw and cow dung) at Kinson called Howe Lodge. When it was demolished in the 1950s it still contained some of the old hiding places.

One such place was a small hiding hole leading to a small room about ten feet up the chimney that was impossible to see from the fireplace. There was also a trap door leading to a secret cellar obviously used for storage, as well as several tunnels leading from the property.

Howe Lodge, Kinson

Isaac Gulliver's empire slowly expanded through his wise investments and in early 1788 he once again had a sizable vacant property to let:

'A neat and convenient Dwelling house, with suitable offices, a good stall stable for horses, necessary out houses, & also a large garden, walled in and stocked with choice fruit trees. A small orchard and two fields adjoining the same. The above is pleasantly situated at Kingston, near Wimborne, Dorset, and fit for the

reception of a small genteel family. A pump with good water in the kitchen.'

Gulliver was also directly or indirectly involved in charity donations.

There is an inscription on a tombstone in the chapel yard of Kinson stating that John Weare, in the name of his daughter Catherine, gave to the poor of Kingston Cudnell, and Ensbury, 10 shillings yearly, to be paid out of his lands at West Moors forever. In the Parliamentary Returns of 1786 this payment is recorded to have been made out of lands in West Moors belonging to Isaac Gulliver.

The property of Mr Gulliver vested, on his death, in Mrs Fryer, whose husband, the late William Fryer Esq. banker at Wimborne Minster was in the habit of paying a small sum yearly to a poor woman, but without specifying that it was in respect of any charge upon his lands.

'By indentures, 31st March 1824 William Fryer conveyed to John Way and two others a piece of waste land on Kinson Heath, at a place called East Howe, containing one acre, in trust for the benefit of the parishioners and inhabitants of Kinson, to be managed and disposed of as they should direct, a building has been erected on this land which is now used as a poor house.'

The Revenue house attack at Blandford

The Bonded Warehouse door being forced open.

It was one of those eerie, silent mornings with no wind and a heavy fog covering Cranborne Chase, when the officers rode out. Every tree they passed looked like ghost appearing out of the mist, their senses were on high alert as they warily approached a small group of buildings after their hard ride, their horses blown.

Somehow, most probably through an over eager lad in a local tavern who had been plied with a few free drinks by an off duty Revenue Office to loosen his tongue, word had reached the ears of the Supervisor of Customs that a cargo of illicit goods was being stored on the road between Blandford and Salisbury, possibly at Thorny Down, one of the abodes of one Isaac Gulliver.

The Supervisor of Customs had his men ready very early on Wednesday morning at the Bonded Warehouse house in Blandford.

One empty wagon, six well-armed men, pistols and rifles checked and loaded, they set off at a fast trot up the hill out of the town heading towards Salisbury. It wasn't long before the riders left behind the wagon that they intended would carry the contraband back to the Supervisors Warehouse.

The weather had been unusually calm for the time of year with a steady south westerly wind blowing, the long gentle swell helping the sailing vessels to make a quick passage from France. Gulliver's ships had been arriving along the Bournemouth beaches with little hindrance from the Revenue Officers recently; large cargos arrived almost nightly during the clement weather and were unloaded and transported speedily inland. The illicit contraband was loaded onto twenty or more wagons each night, and delivered by many experienced 'tubs' men whose knowledge of the heathland inland from the coast was unsurpassed.

This particular shipment of spirits, along with some of the tea, was destined for the local Inns in the area of Handley, Farnham, & Tollard Royal. The tea was normally distributed to the local gentry whose wives kept it under lock and key due to its high cost.

One small band headed towards Gulliver's isolated barn at Thorny Down, on the Blandford road to Salisbury, loaded with some twenty casks of spirits and eighteen hundred weight of tea. They passed through Wimborne early in the morning, only stopping to drop off part of the cargo at one of Gulliver's secret stores.

Taking the Cranborne road they set off to Crichel where a quantity of tea and spirits were unloaded into another barn for later collection, allowing some of the men to leave the convoy and return home. The remainder of the smuggled goods were taken to the small barn behind the Thorny Down house and quickly hidden under a covering of hay & straw.

Gulliver was not a man to leave his cargoes completely unprotected and had employed an 11 year old boy to sleep in the barn. His main duty was to check the road in both directions at dawn, and report to Gulliver if Dragoons, Revenue men, or indeed any unknown person, approached with the intention of entering the property. The lad knew that failure to do so would earn him a severe flogging.

By pure good chance the lad, who had been asleep in the barn loft, happened to look through the small dirty window situated in the eaves of the barn, and was surprised that he could see nothing but a thick fog rolling over the hill into the valley in the distance. He gazed entranced at the beauty of the scene until a movement below caught his eye; something was creeping beside the hedge leading from the road to the barn but in the mist he couldn't quite make out whether it was a deer or something more sinister.

Pressing his face close to the glass, his heart froze as he recognised a red coat in the ditch, possibly two. He scampered down the ladder in an instant. Silently crossing the floor of the barn to a broken panel in the rear wall, he squeezed through it into the damp gloom of the early morning mist. Knowing no one was in the house he crept to the nearby wood stack where he could watch whoever was arriving. Crouching there he saw two Revenue officers approach the side door of the house, one went round to the front, hammering loudly with their rifle butts on the door, calling out for those inside.

"Come out in the name of the King."

Four officers then entered the field through a wicket gate and disappeared inside the barn out of the boy's view. Well aware of the contents of the barn the young lad slipped further away, hugging the hedge that ran to the road where he knew he would have a good view of the officers although he could remain unseen.

It didn't take long for the Officers, shouting and cheering, to discover the casually hidden contraband under the cattle fodder and straw. This would be another feather in the Supervisors cap.

The soldiers carried out the nine casks of spirits and 16 cwt. of tea that had been hidden overnight for distribution to the surrounding Inns in the neighbouring villages, and laid them in the field.

Straining his ears the lad edged cautiously closer listening as the soldiers' voices carried in the mist. He heard enough to realise the contraband would be taken to the Supervisors house in Blandford where it would be stored before onward transportation to the main Poole Bonded Warehouse. Due to the heavy work load over the past few weeks there were no horses in the stables but he needed to escape unseen so he could get word of the raid to Gulliver. He had no choice but to make all haste on foot to Thickthorn a mile away across the fields.

Breathless and soaked after his long run through the fog and wet grass, the lad reached the staging post on the main route back to Blandford. The mail coach had just departed and the Thickthorn groom, who fortunately knew him well, was attending to the four tired horses who had been changed over, gasping the lad cried.

"The Revenue is come; they've found the cache. I have to tell the Master."

"Here, take this old nag, he's reliable and will serve you well, and you won't look out of place on him if you should meet any soldiers.

I've heard tell Gulliver or one of his men might be at Crichel. Best take the footpath not the road."

As he spoke the groom quickly bridled the horse, giving the lad a leg onto its sturdy back.

"Make haste." the groom shouted as he departed.

Before the morning was over the whole of the Crichel and Cranborne area knew the Revenue had captured Gulliver's cargo, but it didn't take him long to formulate plans to recapture 'his' possessions.

Around six o'clock that same day, men from villages all around filled the Blandford Inns. Some of them were permanent employees, Gulliver's White Wigs all would often be unable to feed their families without working for him. They carried a mixture of clubs, blackjacks, and sticks for protection, or to be used in self-defence if necessary.

Shortly before seven Gulliver and Roger Ridout appeared in the town square asking for 'loyal volunteers' to assist him in regaining his 'lawful' goods; promising those who supported him would be well rewarded.

Gulliver rode to the Supervisor's house backed up by a large crowd of men, some on horseback others on foot.

The house appeared to be unoccupied so they secured ropes to the great door of the Supervisor's Bonded Warehouse which it adjoined. A rope was tethered to the door and two horses in traces were encouraged to lurch forward with a flick of the whip across their rumps.

In no time at all the door was forced open.

The casks and tea were quickly retrieved and Gulliver on his white horse surrounded by his White Wigs, shouting and jeering the gang was soon heading out of town. On their way they tossed two casks of spirits to the watching crowd, ensuring that should any Revenue officers try to follow they would be halted by a drunken mob blocking the narrow street up the hill.

Bonded Warehouse door, Blandford

There are no public records showing that this case ever went to the Magistrates court, therefore we must assume a higher Authority overruled the Revenue officers.

Lost revenue

By 1778 Isaac Gulliver was a powerful and prosperous 33 year old man. With the assistance of Roger Ridout, now 42 years old, Gulliver had corrupted many of the local Poole Revenue officers. He held them in the palm of his hand, so that when offered a suitable sum of money they would turn their backs and neither see nor hear anything.

There were two Revenue cutters stationed for the protection of the area, one at Southampton, the other at Poole. The Southampton cutter occasionally made a seizure, but at Poole the Master, Mate, and crew had all been corrupted, and on receipt of certain signals were in the habit of withdrawing to another part of the coast in order to give the smugglers the opportunity to land and carry off their cargoes without interruption.

Confidential reports submitted to the revenue authorities in or about the year 1779 show that some 31 smuggling vessels, of between 20 and 70 tons, and with crews of up to 20 men, were operating along the Dorset coast. During the previous three years these vessels were known to have landed more than 163,000 gallons of spirits and more than 780,000 lbs. of tea. Of the 33 districts into which, for purposes of Revenue administration, England was divided, only one had more vessels operating within it than had the Dorset district, two had smuggled more rum, and three had smuggled more tea.

The duty payable at the time was 4 shillings and 8 pence per gallon on rum and 2 shillings and 3 pence per lbs. on tea. The value of the spirits comes to £38,000, and the tea equates to £87,750, that's a total loss to King George III's government of at least £125,750 over 3 years in Dorset alone (the equivalent of £15 million in today's money) this was an amount that no government could afford to lose. It was money that was urgently required to pay the British Navy to fight the French and Spanish with whom Britain was constantly at war.

Just how much of this lost tax was down to Isaac Gulliver is hard to say, but if the Revenue reports are to be believed and 31 vessels were involved in smuggling along the Dorset coast at this time, and it is reputed by the Revenue office that Isaac Gulliver had up to 15 vessels landing cargoes almost every night, we can say that most likely half the £125,750 lost tax was down to him over three years £62,875 (£7.5 million in today's money). He was certainly the most prolific smuggler on the South coast for 40 or more years.

Of course not all of the money raised through sales was profit. Gulliver had sponsors to repay, ships and crew to hire, some one hundred to two hundred landsmen with horses who needed paying nightly or the following day and, most importantly, his right hand man Rodger Ridout. This was a large enterprise even by modern standards. Only when the contraband was sold would the 'Old Man' know how much he could pocket himself. Running such a large and complex organisation with ships arriving almost nightly in various locations along the coast would have required a nimble brain of great intelligence, as well as a totally loyal and hard working Lieutenant Roger Ridout, without whom this enterprise could not have been so successful. It's hardly surprising that those in power in London were frustrated by this ingenious crook and the revenue they were losing.

A new light on smuggling exploits is given by in conversation which a journalist had with an old seaman then in his ninetieth year who in his younger days had been a smuggler at Portland. This interview was published in the T.P. Weekly May 23, 1903, and the ex smuggler's narrative given as follows :

"I was brought up with the smugglers from a child, and was always helping them either on sea or land, to elude the Preventive officers and to run their cargoes ashore along the coast from Lulworth to Lyme Regis. I remember that one night we had a great haul, and landed 150 kegs of brandy at Church Hope Cove (Portland) After getting this well hidden we landsmen hurried home to our beds, whilst the vessel sailed out again into the Channel; I had not been in bed more than an hour before a Coastguardsman came to my house and inquired if I would come out and help the Preventive officers that night as the lieutenant had received a message that the smugglers were about to run a valuable cargo ashore. I assented as I had already helped to land this cargo and went with him to the lieutenant. I stayed with them some days, and liked my new companions so much that when they asked me to "sign on with them" I consented and was put aboard a Revenue cutter called the Eagle, & a hot time we gave the smugglers, chasing them up and down the Channel confiscating their goods and sending the men to Dorchester Gaol. But the curious part of the whole affair

was that the lieutenant and all of us Revenue men were smugglers ourselves, as we were continually making flying trips across the Channel and bringing home cargo after cargo of contraband goods, landing them without fear of detection, and then sailing out and capturing some poor smuggler who in a whole year never did half the business which we did in a month. Ah, sir, our lieutenant a half pay naval officer was a disgrace to His Majesty's Navy."

This goes to show just how involved the Revenue were in filling their own pockets. It's my belief that Gulliver had them in his pay as can be seen by this statement, they were not above the law themselves.

The Battle of Hookswood

The fight.

It wasn't long before the Salisbury & Winchester Journal had another story to report right on Gulliver's doorstep, and his hand was most certainly involved in this affair which took place not far from the Inn at Thorney Down. The area continued to be a lively centre for smuggling, and in March 1779, at Hook's Wood, about two & a half miles away, there occurred an even more serious affray.

Someone had blabbed. On 'information received' the Excise officer based at Cranborne in Dorset set off one dark night with 6 Dragoons, all armed with guns, swords and pistols to intercept the smugglers. He had it on good authority that some 20 horses or more, heavily laden with contraband, would be passing through Hook's Wood, in the parish of Farnham, that night.

More by luck than judgement, they found the cargo casually hidden in a coppice, where it had been left until it could be distributed around the neighbourhood the following day.

With great delight the soldiers loaded their own horses with the cargo and began to retreat.

However the smugglers had only recently departed for Chettle over the hill and heard the Dragoons helping themselves to the contraband. This would not do. Their very livelihood depended on the successful sale of the cargo; its loss represented a personal loss of income to each and every man. Taking a short cut they were able to intercept the convoy armed with coshes and sticks, between 40 and 50 men attacked the Dragoons, and a dreadful battle ensued, as for the injuries there is no mention in the report that follows. In fact it's a very basic report considering the smugglers beat off the dragoons who were armed with broad swords and pistols while they only had clubs and sticks.

Journal report of the incident:

'The soldiers with their broad swords fought well, and the Excise men fired their pistols.

The smugglers only had large clubs with which to retaliate but eventually they gained the upper hand as they outnumbered the better armed soldiers.

Many men were injured that night but their precious cargo was saved. However several of the smugglers were recognised and two, who were known smugglers, were rousted from their beds in a nearby inn the following morning and committed to Dorchester gaol, where they awaited trial, but were acquitted.'

If they were 'known smugglers' and were acquitted it appears that Isaac Gulliver had protection organised for himself and his men.

The penalties for smuggling were extreme even for that time; execution by hanging, deportation to the colonies, or being pressed into the Navy, as well as long prison sentences were handed down without compassion to any smuggler unfortunate enough to be found guilty.

A Newspaper cutting:

'There is a story told of a certain Dorset lawyer who defended smuggler. After much study and labour he discovered a flaw in the indictment, and the prisoner who otherwise would have been hanged was acquitted.

After a few days after the lawyer on opening his door found on the step a keg of brandy to which was nailed a written paper inscribed "For defending one of our gang." The lawyer secured his fee and said nothing about the affair until some years after.'

Gulliver was now so wealthy that he was able to move from Thorny Down to Longham in Hampshire which he did in 1779. He bought the freehold of a property on the North edge of Bourne Heath, where he was both closer to the sea and which gave him more room for his growing family.

In 1782 Gulliver's continuing prosperity allowed him to buy and live at Hillams Land Farm, Dudsbury, now owned by Dudsbury Golf Club. This house has a large cellar ideal for the storage of wines and spirits. There is what appears to be a bricked up tunnel that seems to lead down to the river Stour, which would have made an ideal secret route to transport goods from the small boats that could make their way up stream from the sea.

The Smugglers' Modus Operandi

Lugger & tubsman

A lugger (small sailing ship with two or three masts and a lugsail on each) could discharge its cargo onto the shore within half an hour of its arrival, weigh anchor, set sail and be away downwind to gather speed before the Royal Navy or a Revenue cutter could chance upon them. Once the tubs of spirits were landed, the tubs-men would carry two tubs at a time in a special harness, designed to hold one tub on the chest and the other on the back. They would lead a fully laden horse or pony with 6 more tubs. The tubs held 4 gallons and weighed 45 lbs. each. These men were strong, agile and fast.

They knew the country well, and could travel great distances independently, dispersing the cargo so as to avoid capture.

It was necessary to transport the tubs far inland overnight to avoid prying eyes of those who might see something they could report.

The pay was 10 shillings per night to each man. The tubs contained raw spirits, the proof being well above a drinkable level and for every twenty tubs one was given free to cover the loss due to waste or evaporation. It made sense to smuggle the spirits unadulterated and dilute it after it had reached its destination.

Diluting the spirits.

After all, there was no tax on water. Once the tubs had been sold to an end buyer, women or sometimes men would then dilute the spirits to 'fire proof' strength by adding water; hence we think of spirits as proof, that is, non-inflammable without added heat.

The casks of spirits were then poured into containers, Glass balls known as 'lovies balls' (hydrometers) were added with different proof strengths etched into them, eg 45%, or 42%. When a 45% ball was placed into the spirit container it would rest on the bottom. Water was slowly added until the ball floated. The liquid was now ready for drinking at 45% proof. The empty casks would then be refilled with the drinkable spirits. The balls were marked with the different proof strengths, as are the bottles today. With the addition of the water, the quantity in the original tub would be almost doubled and could now be sold on to the end user, thus making a hefty profit for the smugglers, and leaving the revenue even more out of pocket.

Vested interests

In 1780, The Earl of Malmesbury's 'Memoirs of an Ex Minister,' tells the story of Lord Shaftesbury & Mr Edward Hooper (Chairman of the Customs) having dinner when Isaac Gulliver and 6 or 7 wagons & horses pass the window at full gallop, the old squire sat still without turning round and continued his meal. When the cavalry arrived he could say he had seen nothing whatsoever, letting Gulliver cross the river and get safely into the New Forest where he could dispose of his treasured contraband.

Mr Edward Hooper, the Chairman of the Customs, was dining in the low hall at Heron Court with his relation, Lord Shaftesbury, and several distinguished guests. A succulent dish of venison had been served and the guests animated conversation was aided by the freely flowing wine. The room full of laughter, when the distant sound of horse's hooves could be heard approaching.

Mr Hooper refusing to turn as the horses pass by.

A great clatter of wagon wheels and galloping horses and grew louder on the gravel track outside the house. The guests craned their necks to see what was causing the clatter and Lord Shaftesbury jumped up to look out of the window as a large number of horses and wagons thundered by in a cloud of swirling dust that hid the wagons as they disappeared round the bend.

The old squire sat at the head of the table with his back to the window. He continued to eat as if nothing had happened, and refused to turn his head to see what was causing the commotion outside. His Lordship returned to his place at the table as the sound faded in the distance. The diners taking their cue from their host, continued with their merriment and dining, the wine continued to flow freely.

No sooner had the dust settled in the road than the diners heard more horses rapidly approaching the house, and loud voices demanding an audience with the Mr Hooper. Eventually Jonas the butler entered the room at a stately pace. After apologizing for interrupting and disturbing his master's repast with his distinguished guests, he leant over the squire and whispered in his ear.

"Sir, the cavalry are at the door."

"Show them in." was the squire's calm reply.

Jonas made his dignified exit before ushering in a hot and agitated officer who spoke with Mr Hooper. The officer explained that he had been chasing a band of smugglers when he had lost them on the main road. He deduced they had taken a turn down the lane that would have led them past this very house. He asked which way they had gone. The guests sat silently, watching the squire as he took a long slow sip of Madeira.

He carefully placed his glass on the table, wiped his lips, and, looking the officer in the eye, truthfully told him that he had seen nothing of any smugglers while he ate his meal. His Lordship, who was sitting at the other end of the table, raised his eyebrows on hearing this, but studiously continued to eat in silence.

The officer left, defeated without the information he so desperately needed. The smugglers made their get away into the New Forest by crossing two deep fords in the nearby river Stour. The soldiers had followed but refused to cross the fast flowing water and so returned to Christchurch empty handed. A few days later a cask of spirits was found close to the house, which was quickly and quietly placed in Mr Hooper's cellar. It must be remembered that Mr Hooper, Chairman of the Customs was an honourable gentleman, and endowed with considerable wealth. Anything in the form of a bribe would have been an insult. Yet he said nothing that might have incriminated Gulliver.

Once again Gulliver's connections with the Harris's, with whom he traded in the Sussex area, had come to his assistance. (Mr Hooper was related to the Harris's by marriage.)

The Earl of Malmesbury also wrote in his memoirs that:

'In the worst period of the war with France, when gold was hardly to be found, a tenant of mine named King, who held a small farm by Cranborne Heath, and who was in arrears with his rent, sent his young daughter with the entire amount of 100 guineas in French Louis-d'ors.'

We can be quite sure that the Earl was extremely happy to receive the rent in gold coins.

Presumably the aforementioned Mr King was a member of the 'White Wigs' one of Gulliver's men, for how else would a 'young daughter' or her father lay their hands on a 100 guineas if not through her father saving his payments from his illegal activities.

One assumes he was either a tubs-man or a highly paid shore man who helped distribute the smuggled cargoes.

The 'White Wigs' were a band of farm labourers, landsmen, and fishermen consisting of between forty and two hundred men employed by Isaac Gulliver to help with the transportation and distribution of his illicit cargos. They were dressed in shepherds smocks and had white wig powder in their hair, thus creating a uniform to encourage loyalty. An offshoot of this was to 'cock a snook' at authority, as wig powder was extremely expensive and could only be afforded by the wealthiest gentry and aristocracy.

Escape from Poole

Gulliver escapes from Poole

With his tricorn pulled firmly down partially shielding the wry smile on his face, Gulliver strode past the customs house on Poole quay. It was necessary for him to visit Poole in order to see his many clients in the various Inns and taverns to take orders or collect outstanding monies for goods delivered. Great care had to be taken as the bounty on his head was worth a year's wages and more to a landsman, this was something he only did on rare occasions, for the Revenue were desperate to catch him. It would be usual for Rodger Ridout to deal with the day to day collection of monies or a trusted employee.

Two Revenue officers were heading his way. Knowing that his great height made him easily recognised, he stepped back into an alleyway out of sight and hurried down a narrow lane before and slipping quietly through a convenient door into a dark passageway.

He stood for a moment, letting his eyes adjust to the dim light while he held the door handle firmly closed and waited until the officers passed. His heart pounded - this was as close as he had ever been to capture.

Having given the Revenue Officers time to pass by, Gulliver opened the door and eased back into the road again before crossing to the King's Head Inn opposite. Startled, he felt a firm hard push on his back forcing him into the gloomy interior of the bar. A small man half Gulliver's height put his fingers to his lips, urging "Old Gulliver" to sit in the corner, out of sight of the door.

"I'm known as 'Slippery.' Slippery Rogers from Christchurch. I run some contraband meself from time to time in my fishing boat. The Revenue are on the quay searching for ye. I heard 'em say they knowed you're here. I recognised you, they will too if they sees you." said Slippery.

"I need to make my escape quickly before I'm found. Can you help?"

" I'll make it worth your while." replied Gulliver.

"I felt sure you would. Never fear, I won't give the game away. Not many would." Slippery said.

"I drink at the Ship most days and know the landlord there buys his spirits from the smugglers, in fact I guess most of Poole does!" he said with a grin.

"But I can't afford to fall foul of the Revenue men or they'll be down on my little fishing boat like a ton of bricks." he added.

"I won't ask you to take risks, but I've had an idea." Gulliver said.

"Can you fetch Mr Martin the landlord to me; he's a regular customer of mine and I'm sure he'll help."

Slippery sidled through the bar and soon returned with the friendly landlord; the three men huddled together, Gulliver issuing instructions.

"Take Slippery and go straight to Mr Dean the brewer.

He's a relation so I know he'll help. Arrange for him to bring the full sized advertising barrel on his dray and wait at the end of the alleyway. Once he's in place, Slippery, you get your crew to block the other end of the alley while I climb inside the barrel. Then the drayman must take me out of town on the Kinson Road. Look lively now my friends and set to it. Here's a guinea apiece now and more later when I make my escape."

Full of nervous energy Gulliver was now on full form again after his narrow escape. The humour in his voice and twinkle in his eyes made men who feared him also love him, so they did his bidding gladly. He grinned wickedly at the thought of out-smarting the revenue men yet again as he slipped into the cellar to await the dray. Mr Martin and Slippery hastened to the brewer.

"We have urgent business with your employer, Mr Dean." they told the gatekeeper.

"Let us in straight away, there's not a moment to lose."

The gatekeeper looked them over dubiously, noting Slippery Rogers' fisherman's overalls, the strong smell of fish which hung about him in a miasma. However he recognized Mr Martin as the landlord of the Kings Head, whom he had seen coming and going in the past, so was persuaded to let them through. On entering the office Mr Martin said.

"Good morning Sir, I have urgent news for you."

Mr Dean raised his hand in acknowledgement, recognizing the landlord.

"Well now Mr Martin what can I do for you that's so urgent."

Looking at Slippery he added.

"And who might you be, my good man?"

"I'm known as Slippery Rogers from Christchurch." Slippery replied without thinking.

"Slippery Rogers? That sounds, well if I may say so, it sounds rather....well - rather slippery- to me!.... So I shall call you Mr Rogers, if I may. What can I do for you both that's so urgent you couldn't wait?"

Lowering his voice, Mr Martin started to explain.

"Mr Isaac Gulliver is trapped in the Kings Head next to the alleyway on the quay. The Revenue men know he's in the town and are out in force, looking for him. I understand that they have also sent for the Dragoons to help with the search. They are determined to find him this time as there's a high price on his head. We have to help get him out of Poole."

"Mmm, very well but how do you propose to do it, and how am I involved in getting old Gulliver out of town."

"Gulliver has a plan, but it involves the dray you use for advertising, the one with the large barrel on it." Martin said with a grin. Slippery started to laugh at the thought of it.

Mr Dean eyebrows shot up,

"You must be mad." he said.

"How can the advertising dray be of any help to old Gulliver? If he drove it out of town, he'd be recognized immediately. There's no chance of it working, I say, no chance at all."

"That's not the whole idea. He plans to ride out of town on the dray but inside the barrel that's used to store the advertising material." Slippery said, grinning at Mr Dean.

"Well I'll be damned. Hmm, it could work you know." Chuckling, Mr Dean said "That would be one in the eye for the Revenue, wouldn't it. Yes, it might just work at that."

"Leave the dray to me, I have to do something for my good friend." Dean said.

"You two go and do what you have to do and I will have the dray outside the Inn as soon as I can. It will take some time, perhaps an hour, less if I can arrange it, but it will be there." He thanked them for coming to him and bid them good day, before rushing to find the brewery manager,

"Send Ben, the old dray man to my office as fast as you can." He instructed the brewery manager.

Meanwhile, the landlord returned to the Kings Head and Slippery went to his fishing boat to collect his crew.

"No questions now, but once you see a dray pull up at that end of the alleyway, I need you to block the other end or cause a diversion should it be necessary." he told them.

Meanwhile, Johnson the brewery manager scolded old Ben.

"I don't know what's going on but the Govn'r Mr Dean wants you in his office right now. I guess it's your retirement time old boy. Jump to it. Don't keep him waiting."

"Will you take me to his office? I haven't been there before." Ben nervously asked the manager.

"Follow me then and look lively, don't bring that bottle with you." The manager said leading the way with old Ben following unsteadily in his footsteps.

When they arrived in the main building they climbed the flight of oak stairs. Ben was frightened as he ascended the sweeping stairway with its many oil paintings hanging on the walls of past generations of the Dean family all seeming to be looking at him. He could not help wondering what lay in wait for him. Mr Johnson knocked loudly at the solid door oak baring his way, making old Ben jump.

"Enter!"

The manager opened the door and pushed Ben through, closing it behind him. Astonished, the old man looked around the wood panelled office which was almost as big as the whole house he rented from the brewery. The intricate carvings and scroll work were a joy to behold and the dark wood glowed in the morning sunlight.

Mr Dean sat behind a solid mahogany desk, so large Ben thought a man could lie flat on the desk without touching the ends. He had never seen anything like it before.

The walls were covered with paintings of horses and more portraits which he guessed were family members. He was just wondering why they all looked so severe when he heard Mr Dean say.

"I want you to take the advertising dray to the Kings Head on the quay, pick up a man, let him get into the barrel, then slowly drive the dray through the centre of Poole. After you've passed through Poole go on to Kinson."

Ben's mind was in a whirl; take the dray to Kinson with an unknown man aboard? The boys had played many tricks on him in the past but this……this was something else…

"Are you listening to me, Ben?" Mr Dean said in a stern voice. "I don't want any mistakes, you understand? Oh, and if the Revenue Officers should stop you give them a drink from the concealed internal barrel, so make sure it's filled before you leave. I mention the Revenue as there are plenty in town today. You are to tell no one of the passenger in the barrel. Do you understand?" leaning forward on his elbows with a slight smile on his face Mr Dean said,

"If you do this well you can stay overnight in Kinson at the local tavern and bring the dray back in the morning. Before you leave I will give you a letter to give to the passenger when you reach Kinson, not before. Be sure not to turn round when you are waiting at the end of the alleyway, just open the secret door under your seat and leave when you are told to. Don't tell anyone here or in town what you are about. Understood? Then that will be all." Dean said, dismissing him with a wave of his hand.

"Make all haste now, don't delay."

"Thank you sir I'll do as you say, sir." Turning, Ben left the room, descended the stairs with the portraits still glaring at him, and made his way to the stables to find a suitable pair of horses to pull the dray.

As Ben walked across the cobbled yard Mr Johnson called him over and asked what had happened in Mr Dean's office.

"I'm not sure sir, but the Governor wants me to take the advertising dray to the quay then on to Kinson, but I'm not supposed to tell anyone."

"In that case don't tell anyone, not even me, you fool. Hurry to the stables and get the two black mares out, they will look good pulling the dray. I'll get the stable boy to harness the horses. Did he say anything else?" Johnson enquired.

"Only that I should have plenty of spirits in the secret compartment the one inside the barrel for distribution on the way."

"Now that is a surprise. Mr Dean doesn't like giving free drinks unless it's for the carnival."

Johnson was puzzled by this order, but knew he would find out later if Ben was telling the truth.

Mr Dean arrived in the yard just as all was made ready and Ben was about to leave.

Looking at his brewery manager he said. "What a wonderful sight, I never tire of seeing good horses, they do us proud."

"I've been thinking," he added. "Johnson, I want you to go with Ben as far as the outskirts of Poole, or if you think it necessary, all the way to Kinson. You are to pick up a passenger on the Quay and transport him in the false bottom of the barrel to Kinson, without anyone knowing he's inside."

Mr Dean walked Johnson away from the dray, "Allow no one to know he is there. Many lives may be at stake." he muttered.

"I want you to serve spirits to the public as you go through the town.

If the Revenue arrive give them some too, but don't let them on board the dray or open the door to the barrel. Is that understood?"

"Yes I understand, but who is the passenger?" Johnson inquired.

"Best you don't know, but he is very special to me so no mistakes, you understand, and no questions either. I'm relying on you." Mr Dean said turning quickly on his heel.

By this time the Revenue Officers had called twice at the Inn but had not found Gulliver who was well hidden in the cellar. He couldn't help but worry about his planned escape; would it work or would they catch him this time?

At last, he heard a wild commotion outside on the quay, lots of noise and laughter, people shouting, loud voices passing in the alleyway.

His spirits rose instantaneously, could everything be working out?

The noise on the Quay was getting louder; it sounded like a drunken crowd, raucous laughter and joking, and then he heard the steady slow walk of horses on the cobbled street. The hoof beats stopped, the babble grew louder. He listened intently, trying to imagine what was happening. A knock on the cellar door startled him. He relaxed when he heard Slippery whisper loudly.

"Come out now."

Gulliver grabbed his coat and unlocked the cellar door. He squinted as he emerged into the alleyway, his eyes rapidly adjusting to the brightness. As he looked around, he saw a group of men slowly coming towards him from the far end of the alleyway, and the dray parked close across the other end, blocking it completely.

He swiftly moved the few feet to the dray, with the group of noisy men behind him.

Unsure who they were he kept moving without looking back. When he reached the dray he hoisted his huge frame into the confined space of the barrel behind the driver's seat, while Ben threw a rug over the trap door.

Noise exploded from the rabble surrounding them, crowds of people rushed past on the other side trying to get to the back of the dray where Mr Johnson the brewery manager was doing his best to hand out free spirits to the boisterous labourers. They all wanted to partake of the free drinks on offer.

The gathering crowd only had eyes for Johnson, handing out the free drinks.

As the dray moved off at walking pace, the group of people followed milling round, taking the drinks that Johnson was handing out.

The crowd grew as word spread. With a crack of his whip Ben pushed on the horses as they rounded the corner into the high street. Wanting to know what was going on, two Revenue officers approached, only to be pushed out of the way by the crowd keeping pace with the dray. Unable to walk and dispense the spirits Mr Johnson climbed onto the back of the dray.

The Revenue men pushed their way forwards, using their muskets to clear a passage through the throng. They asked Johnson why he was dispensing free spirits.

"Tis Mr Dean's birthday," he said offering them an extra large mugful. Fortunately before they could ask any more questions they were swept aside by the inebriated crowd. The dray continued on its way steadily with Ben easing the horses forward through the overcrowded high street.

As they passed a second tavern another group of Revenue Officers appeared heading for the free drinks.

One officer even climbed aboard to try to stop the moving dray, but Ben, remembering his instructions, told the officer to take his turn in the queue and get off the dray as it was the private property of Mr Dean the brewer.

"Ye'll need a warrant to come on board" he said chuckling, playing his part well.

"In the name of the King, Stop! We are looking for Gulliver."

"Look no further then; he's on the dray dispensing spirits to the good people of Poole. If you jump down you'll get your share." Ben replied.

The revenue officer made no move to leave, hanging on to the side of the wagon with one hand and waving his musket in the air, so Ben headed the horses towards the side of the street. The dray hit the curb with a lurch, sending the officer tumbling in a tangle of legs and feet into the crowd, who took delight in giving him a few solid kicks before he could regain his feet.

"Oh sorry sir, 'twas the crowd made the 'orses change direction and me talking to you instead of watching they." Ben touched his forelock as he tapped the nearest rump with his whip.

Two more Revenue Officers, mounted, struggled to make their way through the drunken throng blocking the High Street. The local children took great delight in frightening their horses, making them swirl and prance so the officers could only hang on. The street was in total chaos with the drunken rabble blocking the officers' progress; the alcohol continued to flow.

The procession made slow but steady progress towards the outskirts of town, with Isaac Gulliver lying inside the barrel.

Although he was battered and bruised by the wagon lurching along the road, he enjoyed hearing the commotion going on around him.

Knowing the Revenue men, only a few feet away, did not have the slightest knowledge that he was travelling with them as they walked alongside the wagon consuming more and more alcohol that was being handed to them added spice to his sufferings.

He lay there chuckling to himself as he listened to the conversations going on outside.

Gradually the sound of voices grew less and less. Then a loud voice startled him.

"Ay, Ben that was well done. Poole is far behind now but I shall stay with ye till journey's end." Johnson raised his voice as he spoke, so that Gulliver could hear too.

"Thank goodness the barrel was full; I did fear we might have run out before we left Poole." he added.

Turning his head to look behind, Ben chuckled.

"Look at they Revenue Officers; worse than all the town folk and fishermen put together." he said, watching the officers some way back, staggering, falling, with many drunk.

Ben too shouted out so Gulliver could hear him

"I'm that glad we've left the Officers behind. Now we are free to make all speed to Kinson. 'Tis a long way about 2 hours."

Urging the horses into a trot caused the dray to lurch from side to side and tossing Gulliver about.

Fearing his head would be split open Gulliver called out

"Tis no good; you'll have to walk or there'll be nothing left of me but a broken battered body by the time we reach in Kinson."

Ben eased the horses back to walk and Gulliver closed his eyes and tried to doze in the total darkness, but the discomfort was too great.

The carriages of that era had suspension which dampened down the jolting caused by hard wheels and the uneven surface of the 'roads', even though the subsequent motion could cause a feeling akin to sea-sickness. However farm wagons and drays such as this had nothing to absorb the shocks from the stony tracks and Gulliver must have suffered greatly.

Unable to find a position that suited him for more than a few minutes he was going to ask the driver to stop when he heard Ben call out.

"Oh dear sir. There's a party of Dragoons heading towards us.
What shall we do?"

"Keep still in the back and don't say a word.' Mr Johnson called urgently.

The Officer in charge held up his hand, and Ben slowed the dray to a stop, whereupon small troop of Dragoons surrounded it. Gulliver held his breath as he tried to make sense of the voices.

"Where have you come from, and where are you going?" the Officer demanded.

"We've come from Dean's Brewery in Poole and are on our way to Kinson. We've been giving away free spirits to the good people as 'tis Mr Dean's birthday.." Ben replied.

Johnson said to the Officer. "I have a little left; would you and your Dragoons like to drink to Mr Dean? It's a warm morning and t'will refresh you on your way to Poole."

"Have you seen Gulliver?" The Officer demanded.
Ben replied.

"Who? Who's Gulliver? Why should we have seen him? Nay, we've just been doing as Mr Dean told us, to take the dray to Kinson and dispense spirits to anyone who wanted it on our way."

"Tis beyond me why Mr Dean's would give free spirits away because it's his birthday. He never has before." Johnson added.

"Hmm. Well, I can see Gulliver is not on the dray; however my sergeant and I will take some spirits for our flasks if you please."

The long faced Dragoons looked longingly at the barrel containing Gulliver. The Officer noted their plight and said they could have a tot to be shared between them.

Johnson jumped down and, walking to the back of the dray he proceeded to fill the jostling soldiers' drinking vessels with a very generous tot each.

"I've given you and your sergeant an extra measure for luck." He muttered to the Officer, with a quiet wink.

"I thank you, sir." was the low reply.

Johnson returned to his seat and Ben made the horses walk on, leaving the Dragoons to enjoy their unexpected refreshment.

The journey seemed to take days to Gulliver, squashed into the wooden barrel with nothing to rest on, his feet against the small barrel of spirits that fitted into the rear making it look as though the large advertising barrel contained liquid, but at last the dray finally stopped.

"We're in Kinson, sir, just wait a moment while I open the trap."

Johnson could be heard, drawing back the hidden bolts. Light flooded into the barrel making Gulliver blink in the sudden sun. He needed help to struggle out of the barrel and then lay on his back groaning. Every muscle ached, his head was splitting and his ears were still ringing from the vibration of the dray on the rutted road.

"What a journey." he groaned. "Never again, but hey, it was worth it, wasn't it." he said, rising and clasping both Mr Johnson and Ben by the hand.

"I've never had such a journey in my life, and hope never to again.

But to hear those revenue men and the Dragoons searching for me, and me just inches away........." He started to smile, then, all three men broke into uncontrollable laughter before going their separate ways.

Free pardon

The following proclamation was published in the Gentleman's Magazine

The 3rd of May, 1782, A proclamation was issued granting a free pardon to all smugglers and others under prosecution or liable to prosecution, in prison, or beyond sea, for any penalties incurred by the illegal practices of clandestinely running prohibited or unaccustomed goods, who shall on or before the first day of july next voluntarily enter themselves as sailors on board any ships belonging to the Royal Navy or if they can procure one fit and able seaman and one fit and able landsman as substitutes to serve for him, her or them, provided the penalty to which such persons are liable do not exceed the sum of £500. Those above and under £2000 to find three fit able seamen and three fit and able landmen. Upon which conditions all specified offences are to be forgiven. Likewise his Majesty's pardon to all deserters who shall surrender before the 17th day of June 1782.

Isaac Gulliver took up this option and received a free pardon; it is not known if he paid for his freedom or whether he supplied several seamen and landsmen. Once again luck was on his side.

The Controller of Customs was of the opinion he only continued to smuggle wine and had dropped the tea and spirits. It is more than likely that it suited the Controller to believe this as it made his life that much easier with his superiors in London. Gulliver was wily enough to travel to the west from time to time to give himself an alibi while his ships continued to land their valuable cargos along the Dorset coast probably under the strict eye of Roger Ridout.

It is more than likely the French Revolution, which began some ten years later (in 1792), gave him a further opportunity to smuggle with impunity. With fully laden ships arriving several times a week from France or the Channel Islands, and little or no contraband confiscated by the revenue officers in Poole or Christchurch, reports of Gulliver's activities once again came to the attention of the Kings Revenue Controller in London, who wrote to the distraught Controller Mr Weston at Poole demanding an explanation as to the activities of one Isaac Gulliver.

One can imagine Mr Weston would have a severe case of indigestion when he received that letter from London which landed on his desk just in time to make his Christmas anything but a jolly and relaxed one. His reply is as follows:

Mr Weston's letter to the Controller in London

"In obedience to your order of the 3rd December, for us to report the general character of Isaac Gulliver and the sort of merchandise in which he is concerned we humbly beg leave to inform your honours that but a few years ago the said Gulliver was considered one of the greatest and most notorious smugglers in the West of England and particularly in the spirits and tea trades but in the year 1782 he took the benefit of his Majesty's proclamation for pardoning such offenses and as we are informed dropped that branch of smuggling and afterwards confined himself chiefly to the wine trade which he carried on to a considerable extent having vaults at various places along the coast to the westwards of this port some of which it is said were situated in remote places and we are well informed that he constantly sold wines considerably under the fair dealers price from which circumstances, there is no doubt but

*that he illicitly imported that article but which trade we
are informed he dropped some time since.*

  *He is a person of great speculating genius and besides
the smuggling he has carried on a variety of other
business, but we find he is not known at present to be
concerned in any sort of merchandise and lives retired at
a farm in this neighbourhood having acquired as it is
reported, a very considerable property."*
J.L.R.H.W

Later documents of the time imply that Mr Weston,
Comptroller at Poole, was dismissed from his post in
about 1790, for giving information to smugglers, namely
a John Early, who may well have been a employee or an
acquaintance of Gulliver's. Whilst there is no
verification of this, the job of Comptroller was not well
paid and it would be hard to see a man such as Isaac
Gulliver making a fortune in your territory when you
were paid to have the smugglers under control, if not
locked up in prison. It is quite possible that, like many
in the Revenue, he could have taken bribes to enhance
his life. To witness a man building his property portfolio
under your very nose must have been hard to bear. It
would be easy to imagine that, with his bosses in London
and out of sight, and Mr Hooper at Christchurch most
certainly in constant contact with Gulliver for whatever
reason, Mr Weston would feel he had nothing to lose if
he did his best to fill his pockets without the Revenue
service in London finding out.

  On those occasions when the Revenue decided to make
life more difficult for the local smugglers, Gulliver
would decamp to the West country where members of

the extended Harris family would find him accommodation.

He could thus continue his smuggling activities under their helpful and ever watchful eye.

A Premature death

On one occasion Isaac Gulliver had spent the night on Branksome Chine helping to unload a valuable cargo of spirits, tea and silk from his lugger the Dolphin. Once the contraband was loaded onto horses and wagons he took up a cask of brandy for himself and set forth, leading his convoy of White Wigs through Branksome Woods to the open heath land heading North. The cavalcade passed through the cover of heather and gorse bushes until, tiring of the slow pace of the wagons, Gulliver decided to forge on ahead, leaving his lieutenant, Roger Ridout and William Beale to take control for the remainder of the journey.

About an hour later and some good distance in front of the slow moving convoy, he heard a brutal challenge ring out in the dark from the crossroads a short distance ahead.

"Stop in the name of the King."

Abraham Pike the Riding Officer from Christchurch along with his small troupe of officers, was returning to base at the end of a long and tiring day. He had made the bold challenge in the darkness expecting the unknown rider to stop. Gulliver recognized the voice as Pike's and spurred his still fresh mount into a gallop laughing as he went. Taking a short cut he knew well over the heath to Kinson and home, he lead the Riding Officers away from the convoy of heavily laden slow moving horses and wagons which were following far behind.

Pike, sure he was going to apprehend his quarry, drove his tired mount hard, lashing the poor beast in a vain attempt to overhaul the fast disappearing horse and rider.

Slowly the sound of Gulliver's horse faded into the distance. Pike continued to give chase but was unable to overhaul and arrest him as all the officers' horses were already weary from their long day's work.

Suspecting it could be Gulliver by the rider's size, the tub under his arm, and the colour of his horse, Pike decided to make for Gulliver's House, Howe Lodge, in an attempt to catch him red handed with the keg of spirits.

However Gulliver reached the stable at the rear of the house several minutes ahead of Pike and his Riding Officers, and threw himself out of the saddle at the same time as calling for the sleepy stable boy.

"Boy, come quick. Unsaddle my horse and turn him out in the field behind the stables. Hide the hot saddle under some straw. Be asleep when the soldiers come. If they ask, you haven't seen me for some days and I'm due back tomorrow."

Having thrown the reins to the lad, Gulliver raced in to the house with the brandy keg still under his arm.

Elizabeth was sewing in the parlour as he burst in.

"Pike and his men are close behind. Quick hide me." he gasped.

She jumped up and threw back a small rug concealing a trap door in the parlour floor.

"Down there; quickly and keep quiet, for pity's sake." she urged.

Dropping the tub on the floor, Gulliver leapt down the steps into the cellar below as Elizabeth quietly closed the trap door and replaced the rug.   Then, moving her rocking chair over the trap door she sat with her sewing in her hand composing herself calmly for the Riding Officers' arrival.

Just at the very moment Pike started banging on the front door demanding entry, Elizabeth saw with horror the tell-tale keg standing where Gulliver had dropped it. In an instant she pushed it in front of the rocking chair.

Resting her feet on the keg she allowed her long black skirts to fall around it, concealing the offending item. Elizabeth composed herself once more and, trying to still her trembling hands, continued with her sewing.

Seconds later the maid opened the door,

"Begging your pardon, ma'm" she started to say before an evil tempered Pike followed by several Riding officers burst into the room demanding to know where Gulliver was.

"Where is he? I've just chased him half way across the Bourn heath. I know it was he." shouted a sorely tried Pike,

"I know it was he, I know it."

"You must be mistaken sir. I have not seen him for several days and do not expect him back until late tonight or even tomorrow." She smiled.

Elizabeth dealing with Pike the riding officer.

"I'm sorry, you're wasting your time looking for Gulliver here. You must have been chasing someone else. It most certainly wasn't he."

"If, however, you would like to search the house for him you are welcome, but as you well know you'll have to have a magistrate's warrant to do so." She added almost under her breath, forcing Pike onto the back foot.

Pike knew he couldn't search the house without a warrant so, beaten and very dejected, he turned back to his horse when thought struck him; if Gulliver had just ridden across the heath in front of him his sweating horse would be in the stable.

"I'll have a lamp and light if you please miss." he commanded the maid, determined to search the barn and stables.

Taking his officers with him they entered the stable, where he was sure he would find Gulliver's horse hot and blown from the hard ride home. All he found were several horses who had obviously been in the stables all night, and one single empty box awaiting Gulliver's horse. On hearing the commotion the officers were making, the sleepy stable boy climbed down from the hayloft above.

"Who are you, sir and what are you doing in my Master's stables?' he asked, rubbing his eyes in the lantern light.

"I'm Officer Pike and I ask the questions, lad. Now, where is the missing horse who should be in this stable?

"My Master has him sir, and I don't expect him back till the morrow."

"I know he's here somewhere. Never fear, I'll be back and I will find him." Pike swore as he mounted his horse and led his band back to Christchurch.

True to his word, the following day, warrant in hand, Abraham Pike made all possible speed to Howe Lodge. He knocked on the door and was received by a tearful maid.

"Oh, sir, oh dear, sir." she sobbed and sniffed, "You'd best come in sir. I'll take you to the Mistress."

Pike was taken aback to see Elizabeth apparently in a state of shock, dabbing her moist eyes.

"Pray tell me, what has happened to cause you such distress?" like many men the sight of a lady's tears was too much for him to maintain his anger.

"Oh sir, such dreadful news." Elizabeth tearfully informed him.

"My husband Isaac came home late last night, after you had left, and then he died in his sleep. He's up there now, lying in state in his bedroom. It took several strong men to lay him out on his bed due to his great size." Elizabeth held her hankie to her eyes.

"I hope it's not presumptuous of me to ask, but could I please view the body?" Pike asked

"Well, I don't know, it's not really proper." Elizabeth demurred.

"I do have a Magistrates Warrant, allowing me to search the house and premises, but if I can see Gulliver's body, I shan't need to search." Pike was gently insistent.

"Very well." Elizabeth said, summoning the maid.

"Show this gentleman upstairs."

Gulliver in the coffin

Pike was shown into the dimly lit room where he saw the body of Gulliver lying in a coffin dressed in his burial cloths, his face deathly white, and a penny on each eye. He stepped back in horror, never having seen a dead body lying in a coffin before. Stammering, he managed to apologize for intruding while the family was in mourning, muttering his condolences as he beat a hasty retreat from the house.

His spirits rose as he rode away from the house, knowing he would have to enter this episode in the records as another defeat for the Revenue, but at long last Isaac Gulliver's smuggling reign was over as far as the Revenue was concerned. He foresaw his life would become somewhat less frantic now Gulliver had departed this world.

Elizabeth watched the officers' retreat from an upstairs window and when the coast was clear and the sound of Pike and his Officer's horses had faded, Gulliver climbed out of the coffin letting the light covering of white wig powder that covered his face fall to the floor.

Elizabeth burst out laughing at the sight of her husband and they rejoiced at the misfortune of a defeated Pike.

However they had not realised how quickly news of Gulliver's death would spread throughout the region, even causing the parson to arrive to discuss the funeral arrangements. They realised there was no turning back now for Elizabeth or Isaac, a funeral would have to be organised. Thus the funeral took place several days later with the coffin filled with stones, lying in the central aisle at St Andrews Church, Kinson.

Pike attended the funeral, keen to see the end of his nemesis.

From his place near the door he was amazed to see that the church was unable to hold all the mourners, and the large congregation spilled out into the church yard. Isaac Gulliver had been an important benefactor to many in the region and would be a sad loss to all. The coffin was carefully laid to rest in the old tomb that the smugglers used to conceal their contraband. Elizabeth said it was where he wished to be buried in front of a sobbing group of family, friends and mourners, none of whom were aware that the stone filled coffin didn't contain their friend and master.

For Gulliver had left the area the very day of his supposed demise and he wisely stayed away for several months until the clamour had well and truly died down.

Before returning to his home in Kinson he made a short visit to Wimborne some months after 'his' funeral to conclude various business matters, where he walked through the market dressed as a farm worker.

He only stayed in the area for as sort a time as possible, carefully keeping a low profile from the ever watchful Revenue officers.

Disguising his huge bulk was not easy, but a small pebble in one shoe, a walking stick, long bulky clothes and a stoop made a good disguise while he was in the town. Gulliver eventually removed to Tingmouth, Cornwall, leaving Kinson altogether and giving his customers only about 5 weeks advance notice. This was not unusual for Gulliver as he had to keep on the move while the Revenue were on his heels. Once again his cunning mind kept him one jump ahead of the game.

Gulliver man of wealth

Catla Volcano erupting

Isaac Gulliver found he had an excess of money that he couldn't legally account for. The wealthy gentry of the area had sponsored him, helping pay for his shiploads of contraband which, according to the Revenue officers along the Bourne and Devonshire coast, arrived almost nightly. Profits accumulated rapidly. Gulliver had to think of ways of using his cash legally. He began by lending money on mortgages at about 4½%. This brought in a good return with the added prospect of acquiring more land should a mortgage fail to be redeemed in due time.

In 1783 the most appalling catastrophe happened in Iceland, a far off country that was unknown to Isaac and many of the people of these islands and most of Europe.

Mount "Catla" erupted with one of the most powerful explosions known in modern times. It pumped millions of tons of ash high into the atmosphere which drifted south east over Britain and Europe. The eruption continued unabated for two years with the resulting Sulphur Dioxide choking and slowly killing some 30,000 people in Britain. France and Germany were also covered in the thick choking invisible Sulphur Dioxide, with the volcanic dust blocking out the sun. Throughout northern Europe, crops failed for several years causing a great famine and many to starve to death. It is estimated that over a million people died. The consequent lack of food and work could have been the final straw that started the rebellions in France, leading to the French Revolution.

In England, more and more disgruntled farmhands, labourers and other lowly paid families fell further into poverty. Such men needed well paid or part time work to feed their families, and they couldn't afford to be too fussy as to its nature. These desperate men were easy targets for Gulliver and his henchmen to recruit, swelling his army of 'White Wigs.' When several ships arrived on the Bourne coast at the same time some 200 men or more were required to disgorge the illicit cargo. So many were desperate to put food on their tables that breaking the law was almost irrelevant, for done it must be, mouths had to be fed. Is it any wonder that the few Revenue officers or the one small troop of Dragoons stationed in the area were unable to apprehend and confiscate this much valuable contraband. Those 'lucky' enough to work for Gulliver were not going to jeopardize their main form of income to turn King's Evidence. Most likely, some officers of the crown even fell to the temptation of a gold sovereign or two to turn a blind eye.

The French Revolution: when fortune smiles on Gulliver

Details of the French Revolution have no place in this history, but a short explanation is necessary to show its importance to smugglers on the south coast of England, and Isaac Gulliver in particular.

Fortune smiles on all of us from time to time, some more so than others. Isaac Gulliver seemed to have his fair share of luck and more, as the many stories passed down through the generations show. In 1789 the French peasants were restless; there was much talk of revolution and before long rebellion against the King and monarchy took place. Louis XVI was captured, held in prison and finally executed in September 1792 along with many of the French nobility.

Doctor Guillotine had for some years been trying to get the government to switch to a better and more efficient way of execution. He had seen etchings of an ancient machine used by the English for a short period in the 13th or 14th century that cut criminals heads off cleanly with the drop of an axe head between two vertical wooden posts, with the prisoner secured at the base.

The newly formed National Assembly in France accepted this system of execution, even if it was a repetitive proposal by the Marquis Lepeletier de Saint-Fargeau, decreeing that "Every person condemned to the death penalty shall have his head severed."

Doctor Guillotine advocated this method of execution should be standardized throughout France, the traditional methods such as sword or axe could and did prove messy and difficult, especially if the executioner missed or the prisoner struggled as many did and several blows were required to sever the head. A machine would not only be fast, it would be quick and reliable.

The Terror

In 1793, political events caused a new governmental body to be introduced: The Committee of Public Safety. This was supposed to work quickly and effectively, protecting the Republic from enemies and solving problems using 'necessary force'; in practice, it became a dictatorship run by Robespierre. The committee demanded the arrest and execution of "anyone who either by their conduct, their contacts, their words or their writings, showed themselves to be supporters of tyranny, of federalism, or to be enemies of liberty." One could go so far as to say that the new laws covered many of the wealthy and most of the noble families of France.

From 1793 Madam Guillotine, as she became known, was working overtime in the Place de Concorde, Paris.
Blood stained the cobbles red, and it is written that the Seine also ran red on some days until the end of the revolution. The aristocracy and nobility fled France, heading mostly to Germany and England. Those who could lay their hands on the necessary money and had the contacts to cross the channel preferred England where they felt safer than Germany. If they were caught fleeing they were unceremoniously taken back to Paris to

be publicly humiliated and taunted before walking up the steps of Madam Guillotine.

The lucky ones would give a gold coin to the executioner as a bribe to finish the job cleanly. The prisoners would be forced face down onto a board with their head protruding, strapping them securely in place the board was pushed forward so the neck was under the blade. A last prayer was allowed, the executioner gave the rope securing the blade a tug. With a resounding crash the blade passed through the victim's neck allowing the head to tumble into a straw filled basket below. Blood squirted several feet forward from the neck until the heart finally gave out. The crowd cheered loudly and history reports that women at the front continued with their knitting, although occasionally splattered with the hapless victim's blood.

It's not surprising therefore that many people of noble birth fled the country over the following years, as they knew that they too would have an appointment with the terrifying Guillotine should they be caught.

Isaac Gulliver's ships along with many smugglers, had been carrying secret messages back and forth across the channel between France and England for a year or more, he became increasingly involved with the French revolution. This line of business proved to be extremely profitable for him. Amongst others, there were letters for the Duchess of Devonshire, a leading lady in the underground movement connected to the French spy system.

She travelled extensively throughout France gathering information which she then sent back to the British government.

Parliament was as usual busy dealing with the day to day running of the country, making new laws and keeping an ever watchful eye on the French and Spanish.

They were happy to use all means possible to convey secret letters back and forth across the English Channel and thus many smugglers became involved. Those in power knew full well the smugglers had excellent contacts along the French coast who were used to keeping secrets and had many hiding places, therefore what better way to carry secret documents between England and the French spies without raising the suspicions of the French authorities.

During 1790 reports reached England that the French population was becoming restless. It appeared that Louis XVI's life was in some danger along with all the Nobility of France. The French Revolutionary Wars started in 1792 and ultimately featured spectacular French victories that facilitated the conquest of the Italian peninsula, the Low Countries, and most of the territories west of the Rhine, achievements that had defied previous French governments for centuries. Internally, popular sentiments radicalized the Revolution significantly, culminating in the brutal Reign of Terror in 1793 - 1794.

After the fall of Robespierre and the Jacobins, the Directory assumed control of the French state in 1795 and held power until 1799, when it was replaced by the Consulate under Napoleon Bonaparte.

A constant stream of information passed between The Duchess of Devonshire and Lafayette in France regarding the explosive situation in France. The Duchess spent much time in France and became extremely worried by the behaviour of the population.

The information she frequently passed back to the English government kept them informed of the increasingly volatile situation. Many such messages were sent directly by smugglers on their daily crossings including Gulliver.

The French authorities happily allowed the smugglers access to their ports; as far as they were concerned they were getting English gold for French goods. This in turn reduced the amount in taxes paid to the British government which were required to pay the British Navy in order to keep the French and Spaniards at bay.

One assumes the French were unaware of the constant stream of letters passing across the channel at the same time, keeping the British government informed of the situation as it evolved in France.

Likewise the smugglers carried a constant flow of information from England providing the French with much required intelligence on the British government's position, as well as the latest news on the French Court.

It was a situation made in heaven for the smugglers; they were being paid by both sides and lining their pockets at the same time.

Late one night after the day's business had been concluded in the House of Lords, a select group of Peers held a private meeting. The Duke of Dorset brought the meeting to order and told the group that a Revolution in France was well under way. The Whigs were backing the revolution. This small group of peers were sworn to secrecy; word must not escape in case it should somehow fall into the hands of the wrong authorities either in England or France.

Several Peers at a secret meeting were related to the French aristocracy by birth or marriage and were already aware of the worsening situation across the channel.

They had received letters from France, some via the Duchess of Devonshire, stating that their counterparts wanted refuge in England. With their lives in danger, the French émigrés had to leave their homes hastily and in disguise, and secretly travel to the sea ports in the north of France, desperately hoping not to arouse suspicion of the revolutionaries. Plans were drawn up by this small and powerful group of nobility, which could be immediately enacted upon should the situation worsen.

Over several weeks of such secret meetings, it was established that a number of Peers had had dealings with, or heard of, Isaac Gulliver; enjoying the fine tea, spirits, and wonderful bolts of cloth and silk their wives were particularly fond of that seemed to arrive on their estates as if by magic. It's fair to say that some even sponsored him. He was known to be a man who worked in total secrecy, with a small fleet of ships at his disposal which crossed the channel almost daily.

They had access to Revenue documents which proved his ability.

His contacts with the merchants at the French & Channel Island sea ports were unsurpassed, and they were totally loyal to Gulliver as he had brought much trade to them over the years. He was known affectionately as "Le Contrebandier" in the northern sea ports as his activities had created great wealth amongst the local French warehouse owners.

This small powerful group of peers noted all this to their satisfaction, they soon formulated a plan that they felt sure Isaac Gulliver would be unable to resist, but which left them unidentifiable.

Some months later the Revolution started in earnest. One day after being convicted of conspiracy in 1792 King Louis XVI was sentenced to death by the French National Convention. His execution by guillotine took place in the Place de la Revolution in Paris. King Louis XVI was executed along with many of those in positions of power in his court. The plan that had been formed earlier by the Peers in England was put into action after a request came from France for the safe and secret passage to England by a person of noble birth. This had to be carried out by the English, and not the French, as the aristocrats' lives could not be guaranteed, should any French revolutionary become aware of it. Family legend has it that because Gulliver apparently sent messengers to London to report the possible invasion of the Spanish fleet, or of Napoleonic ships threatening to invade England, King George III said "Isaac Gulliver should

The execution of Louis XV1

be given a free pardon and he should be allowed to smuggle as much as he liked."

However there is no trace of any such document, either official or unofficial at the records office at Windsor Castle, and other record offices.

Nevertheless the following stories would appear to hold much more credence and have been passed on to me by Peter Harvey from his grandmother's (Mrs Louisa Jane Harvey nee Harris) notes.

It wasn't long before a letter arrived for Isaac Gulliver with the following instructions.

"Isaac Gulliver is to set sail for Jersey at the earliest possible opportunity; once there he is to remain in the port until a rendezvous can take place at a designated

Lugger loading passengers escaping the Revolution

address. Francois- Rene, Vicomte de Chateaubriand, a soldier is to be transported safely and in secret to the English coast. A sum of money in gold Ecus will be paid by the Vicomte in full for the voyage, and safe deliverance to English soil. The Vicomte stayed in England, after which he set sail for the Americas.
Chateaubriand took advantage of the amnesty issued to émigrés to return to France in May 1800, he died in Paris in 1848.

During the revolution years Isaac Gulliver received several more requests help. His ships had transported Francois- Rene, Vicomte de Chateaubriand and his family to London. (Source: Peter Harvey's family)

Francois- Rene,   Louis, Marquis de Fontains
Vicomte de Chateaubriand

Obviously pleased with the success of these rescues, which were completed without hindrance from His Majesty's Navy or the Revenue Officers, another request was sent to Gulliver.

This time safe passage to England was requested for Louis, Marquis de Fontains and his friend Suard a 'counter revolutioner.' whose lives were in danger for plotting against the revolution. They both made a safe passage to England and travelled on to London and the USA.

The Marquis' life was spared some years later when he returned to Paris where Napoleon commissioned him to write an essay on Washington, USA.

As Napoleon said.
"They (the English) have the courage and ability to do anything for money."
"Those with other particular problems found the smugglers helpful too."
Napoleon was also heard to say at a later date.

"I couldn't have fought the wars in Europe without the British gold."

He was, of course, referring to the smugglers and their fleets of vessels crossing the channel on their daily voyages who paid for their goods with gold coins.

Life took on a new direction for Isaac Gulliver who, along with many other smugglers, was being paid a fortune in both gold and jewellery, giving safe passage from France to those that could afford it. It is unlikely he ever crossed from France or the Channel Islands to the English coast without an aristocrat sitting on top of a hold full of contraband during those stormy years of the Revolution, thus giving him a double payment for each trip, one for the cargo and another by the escapees.

If, at that time, he was met on the high seas by one of his Majesties' ships who intended to board him, we can only imagine the arrogant grin with which he would have told them who he was, and that he was on the Kings business. The disgruntled captain would have no choice but to give him a wave and send him on his way.

We of course will never know just what happened, but something along those lines must have taken place.

It's no wonder Gulliver happily took on this clandestine task and that his smuggling activities seemed to become less frequently reported during the second half of the 1790's. His "free" passage across the Channel must have made a considerable difference. We will never know how many trips to France he made, nor how many families he assisted in fleeing from the clutches of the

French Revolution along with other smugglers, but we do know that he also carried secret documents and letters, which earned him huge sums of money in gold coinage over a number of years.

It appears from the records that during these trips Gulliver experienced no hardship or harassment from either the Revenue or the Navy who were continually patrolling the Channel hunting for smugglers. It seems more than likely that officers were warned by The Chairman of the Customs that Gulliver's ships must be given 'FREE PASSAGE' as he carried out his secret missions for the state. Gulliver's fleet of ships crossed to France or the Channel Islands almost daily. Although the Navy and the revenue ships were constantly at sea looking for - and catching - many smugglers, there is no mention of Isaac Gulliver running foul of any ship flying the Kings flag during these years.

There is another possible theory about the Free Pardon given to Isaac Gulliver. That is the knowledge that he gained of France from his pursuits became very useful during the Napoleonic Wars, he placed this knowledge at the disposal of the Government of the day.

The Hope Diamond

Gulliver's escapades may also have involved the Hope Diamond, as it's now known (currently in the Smithsonian Museum, Washington, USA).

The diamond was discovered in India in the seventeenth century by Monsieur Tavernier whilst prospecting for precious gem stones.

Jean Baptiste Tavernier

He specialized in gems and was renowned for finding a magnificent large blue diamond of 112 carats uncut. On his return to France he sold the recently cut diamond to Louis XIV, the Sun King, who was also a great collector of such gems. The now cut sixty seven carat stone became known as the "French Blue" and was the only known large blue diamond in existence at the time.

This magnificent diamond was kept by the French Royal family in the Paris Jewel House until the Revolution.

In November 1791, our famous poet William Wordsworth visited France and became fascinated with the Republican movement. He fell in love with a French woman, Annette Vallon, who in 1792 gave birth to their child Caroline. During his time in Paris he became acquainted with The Duke d' Orleans whom he later assisted in fleeing the country, by disguising himself as Wordsworth's assistant.

John Harvey

Around this time the Duke contacted his good friend John Harvey of Ickwell Bury, Bedfordshire, who was the commander of a regiment called the Bedfordshire Yeomanry Horse Artillery and who was visiting his cousin William Harris at Muckleshell in the parish of Holdenhurst, Dorset. Both John and William were distant cousins of the Duke, so The Duke's request for their assistance in helping him escape revolutionary torn France was natural. William Harris and John Harvey disguised themselves along with the troops by traveling with a small circus group comprising of clowns and acrobats. Gulliver, and the Harris family, were involved in the smuggling trade in Devon & Cornwall, arranged their voyage across the Channel to France.

Arriving in Paris John Harvey with the travelling circus and his small troop of men quickly made contact with the Duke d'Orleans.

They formed a rescue plan which included the theft of the Crown Jewels that were housed in the Garde Meuble de la Couronne.

The break into the jewel house

Several of the acrobats managed break some windows in the building thus entering to the jewel house where they created a distraction while others, using a key, gained access to the inner sanctum. Meanwhile outside the crowds were entertained by the clowns and rest of the circus. The thieves removed a large quantity of jewels from the building and made good their escape.

It was now that William Wordsworth came into his own. He had made friends with many of the revolutionaries who were familiar with the old Roman stone quarry tunnels that spread for some 22 miles under the city. The fugitives were led deep into these tunnels and effected their escape.

However, as with most guerrilla troops, the two factions fell out and the young French activists took their payment and disappeared, leaving Harvey totally lost with his troops deep in the underground maze of tunnels. Fortunately Wordsworth and his young mistress Annette Vallon found them and were able to lead them to the outskirts of Paris.

The Duke fleeing Paris

At last they reached the waiting coaches and horses and Harvey, his troops and the Duke made all haste back to the safety of the coast, the Duke clutching the remaining stolen boxes of jewels which possibly contained the French Blue. They boarded Gulliver's ship, the Marianne which had been moored in port awaiting their return. Setting sail he then took them safely back to Christchurch. Records show the Duke d'Orleans lived at Priory House, Christchurch, as a refugee from the revolution until about 1807.

In 1812, twenty years after its arrival in England a Blue Diamond of forty five carats turned up in London, (the original stone would have been cut again to disguise it) and went on public display. This gem was later owned by King George IV who named it the London Blue. It can be seen in some of his portraits hanging from his neck.

The Hope Diamond

We don't know of any other large blue diamonds in the late 1700s, or early 1800s so it is quite possible that the London Blue began life as the French Blue, cut down to disguise its doubtful provenance.

We can only speculate whether this magnificent stone crossed the channel in the hands of a French nobleman fleeing for his life.

However it is unlikely that such a valuable gem would have been used to pay Isaac Gulliver for the safe crossing from France. We can only speculate that the Duke, brother of the King of France, Louis XVI, carried it to London and sold it to a dealer to raise money to provide for his family. It could then finally have made its way to George III who on hearing how the Duke escaped, may have given Isaac Gulliver a Pardon allowing him to "smuggle as much as he liked." There are many theories to the 'pardon' if he ever was given one.

There are no written records relating how the jewel found its way to London. On the death of George III the stone passed to George IV, who was unable, or unwilling, to say how it arrived in his possession. One fact is most definitely true: the French Blue crossed the channel after the start of French Revolution and before 1812, which was when Isaac Gulliver was transporting aristocrats and letters from spies to safety. It is known he was well acquainted with the Duke of Orleans' family, (the Harveys) and possibly the Duke himself.

In 1812 John Françillion wrote a memo documenting the presence of a Blue Brilliant diamond in London. He believed it to be the French Blue Diamond. It was in the hands of one Mr Daniel Eliason, a London diamond merchant. This diamond was without any provenance, with no account being rendered as to where it came from. There are no records of its travels and fortunes before George IV acquired the stone. Sir Thomas Lawrence painted a portrait of George IV wearing the insignia of the Royal Order of the Golden Fleece which was set with a large blue stone, believed to be the French Blue.

When George IV died in 1830, the stone was sold to pay off his debts. It was lost again until a slightly smaller Blue Diamond came up for auction some years later, a 'fabulous blue diamond' was entered in the gem collection catalogue of Henry Philip Hope in 1839. If this was indeed the French Blue, it would have been cut and recut every time it changed hands, in order to disguise it as was normal practice in those days.

Banking

This wily, cunning middle aged man was drawing near to his fiftieth birthday with three children, how could he secure their futures? Elizabeth, Ann, and his son Isaac. He now set to work to find a suitable suitor for Elizabeth. By now he was rich beyond his wildest dreams, his cunning had secured him a vast fortune along with a property empire stretching across Dorset and into Hampshire. He soon found the answer in an acquaintance by the name of John Fryer a local banker who just happened to have a son, William Rolls Fryer exactly the same age Elizabeth.

This wily old fox who had led the Revenue a merry dance for many a long year, who caused the Comptroller of Customs Mr Weston to lose his job in Poole, the Christchurch Riding Officer Abraham Pike to believe he was dead and miss the most important arrest of his career was to set a matchmaking meeting between William Fryer, of Lytchett House, Nr Poole, and Elizabeth his daughter. The Fryers were an extremely well connected family as John Fryer, the banker, was the nephew of Sir John Fryer a past Lord Mayor of London. In due time the two were married with seven children, Gulliver was now so well protected he could use the two 'family' banks with immunity and safely retain his money.

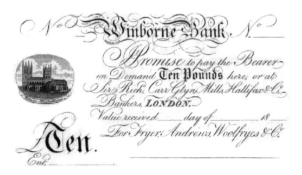

Fryer, Andrews, Woolfyes & Co. £10.00 note.

John Fryer had set up the private bank known as, Fryer, Andrews, Woolfrey & Co, with John Fryer, John Andrews and William Woolfrey as directors in 1790.

A 1797 list of country bankers lists Fryer & Co as bankers at both 'Wimborne and Poole'. It was also known at some time as the Wimborne, Poole & Blandford and Dorset Bank. By 1840 it had branches at Poole, Ringwood, Blandford, Wareham and Sturminster Newton. Also there was a second family bank with William Castleman, attorney in Wimborne, who along with William Dean & George Adams set up the Christchurch Ringwood and Wimborne Bank in 1800.

William Castleman was also closely connected to Isaac Gulliver by marriage to his granddaughter. What better way for Gulliver to launder money than through the 'family banks.'

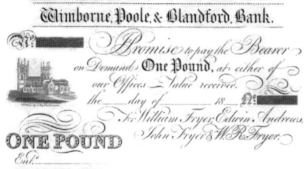

Wimborne, Poole & Blandford Bank £1.00 note.

At that time the Bank of England reported that capital of at least £20,000 to £25,000 was required to become a banker. Ann, daughter of William Rolls Fryer, married Edward, son of William Castleman, a director of that bank. Both banks were acquired by National Provincial Bank of England in 1840.

In 1750 there were only 12 banks in England but by 1797 this number had grown to some 250. It is interesting to note that the Christchurch, Wimborne and Ringwood Bank, founded in 1789, issued its own bank notes that were payable on demand in the coinage of the realm.

By 1808 all banks issuing paper money required a licence which could only be obtained by proving the bank had the necessary bullion to cover the notes in circulation. What a wonderful way to use Isaac

Gulliver's Guineas, gold Ecus, and Louis d'Ors from his earlier French transactions.

Wimborne Bank £5 note.

The National Provincial Bank Ltd, Poole, took over the Fryer Andrews & Co Bank in 1841, it is thought this had been a counting house since 1665. Records indicate that the merchanting business of Fryer, Andrews was carried out near the Corn Market in 1740. One of their customers was our 'old friend' Isaac Gulliver who had easy access to money in the centre of his activities.

A draft advertisement for the post of accountant in the Fryer Andrews Bank written by William Fryer dated December 30, 1815.

'He would be found a house room. Fire, candles, and lodging, with a person to provide victuals, clean house, etc, provide he (1) could provide security to £20; (2) was good accountant, steady and sober; (3) was of good address, civil and pleasant to the customers of the bank. The hours of business were to be from six in the morning in summer, till eight o'clock in the evening if the

business and books were not finished before say from March 25 to September 30 and from eight o'clock in the morning in the winter to eight o'clock in the evening or later if the books and accounts were not finished.

Many newly formed banks failed to redeem their notes in coins of the realm and went into liquidation. The Christchurch, Wimborne and Ringwood bank stayed prosperous throughout its life as a privately owned bank, although it had several name changes, finally becoming the Fryer, Andrews & Co Bank (1790-1840) (it ceased to trade only after it was taken over by the National Provincial Bank in the 1840).

Around the early 1800's the bank ventured into lending money to those beneficiaries of the Enclosure Act. In 1802 the Enclosure Act allowed land to be given to individuals who, in the eyes of the commissioners, had a historical right to the common land, and were also known to be good and loyal citizens to the King. The Christchurch, Wimborne and Ringwood bank lent 'awards', particularly to those of the liberty of West Stour, otherwise known as The Liberty of Westover. It took a further three years to create the Award. By 1805 the beneficiaries so named were given full ownership of their plots of land to develop as they wished. So began the process of building on the heath that formed Bournemouth, which has further grown to form the large urban expanse of development that we know today.

Cornish Tin Mines

Notes from Mrs Louisa Jane Harvey (nee Harris)

Over the years Isaac Gulliver had plied his extremely successful trade from Sussex to the far reaches of Cornwall. In particular he, with Roger Ridout, used the St Michael's Mount region of the Cornish coast, where many discreet coves were hidden along its extensive coast line. This part of the coast was owned by the St Albans family. From the mid 1700s to the early 1800s, the island was mostly uninhabited. The Harris family, agents to the St Albans, used the island as a "holiday home."

The Cornish branch of the Harris family were also "Agents" for much of Cornwall. Arthur Harris of Hayne was the governor of St Michaels Mount. Thus, they controlled most of the local activities of farming, boat building, fishing and smuggling - as well as appointing the law upholders. It is reported that during the Elizabethan wars with Spain as well as during earlier conflicts, 'Buccaneers' used many of the disused tin mines to hide their 'treasure' until such time as it could be safely disposed of. From time to time their ships would be lost at sea, or the crew would be captured and possibly executed, leaving such 'treasure' hidden in the mines, lost and buried forever.

The Harris family had been involved in the Buccaneering trade during the reign of Elizabeth I, and thus dealt with the pirates, allowing them to acquire some of their treasure and gold. They spent the spoils building ships and fishing vessels, which brought employment to the ship yards and local community.

Some of this money trickled down to farmers and landsmen as well. This largesse continued for the many decades of the wars with France and Spain, giving the locals a small but steady income which kept poverty from their doors.

The recovery of lost treasure

Notes from Mrs Louisa Jane Harvey (nee Harris)

When the Bourne region was too "hot" for Isaac Gulliver and Roger Ridout they left that part of Dorset for a few months. Sailing fully laden with spirits, tea, cottons and silk they departed the Channel Islands to the Devon coast. Early that evening the wind died, and a rising tide forced them up the channel. Start Point was breaking the horizon far on the beam when the lookout shouted that he could see the tops of what looked a Revenue cutter far out to sea.

With the fickle evening wind dying away, neither vessel had any steerage. Both vessels wallowed helplessly as their useless sails flogged and the rigging slapped the masts as they rolled.

The sun slowly sank behind the hills leaving the two rivals far apart and finally lost to each other. Darkness fell leaving only the stars to steer by. Both crews spent a tense cold night, straining to see through the blackness.

As dawn approached, zephyr breezes ruffled the surface of the calm sea. The sails filled, masts creaked and groaned as the rigging took the strain, the smuggler's lugger started to heal gently leaving a phosphorescent trail in the calm dark water. Gulliver and Ridout decided to head west, in the opposite direction to that planned.

With the ebb tide now under her and a light wind blowing, the old lugger made good headway, hugging the Cornish coastline to reduce the likelihood of being seen.

Although the light winds remained steady the smugglers had another whole day's sail to reach a safe haven in Cornwall, a much longer voyage than was originally planned.

At last St Michael's Mount came into view, where a young farm hand stood on the headland high above signalling. He had recognized the old lugger even though its master hadn't visited them for several years. Soon the lad was lost to sight as he raced off to warn the villagers of the ship's imminent arrival.

Gulliver breathed a sigh of relief as he brought the Marianne into wind, and ordered her sails dropped, while the anchor disappeared into the crystal clear water.

Already several small fishing boats were setting off from the shore to meet them, and the crew disgorged her cargo quickly into the fleet of boats until the lugger rode high on the lazy swell.

Then Gulliver went ashore to meet the local agent, who was under the direct control of the Harris family. The steward led a band of locals up winding paths to a disused tin mine which had been used as a hiding place in the past. The cargo of illicit spirits, tea, and silks quickly disappeared deep into the poorly lit tunnels well out of sight of prying eyes. Gulliver, Ridout and the local agent were standing talking at the mouth of the mine when they heard cries from far inside the dimly lit smoke-filled passages.

The buried chest

The cries and shouts grew louder and more urgent as the three men entered the tunnel which was lit only by a smoking torch.

Fearing a calamity, they dashed into the tunnel lit only by the flickering light of the smoking torches. Arriving deep inside the mine they found a group of men on their knees digging frantically with their bare hands at the base of the tunnel wall, surrounded by a litter of casks, cases, and silks discarded on the earthen floor where they had dropped them in their excitement.

The men had stumbled upon the top of a metal bound wooden chest partially buried under rocks and sand. It seemed that a recent rain storm may have flooded the long-disused shaft, washing the sand away and exposing the corner of an ancient chest long since forgotten. Further digging finally unearthed the locked chest which was then transported to the Agent's house by cart. A local lad was sent running to tell Mr Harris of the find.

The locks were forced open by the local blacksmith in the presence of Mr Harris. The contents of the chest saw daylight for the first time in many a long year.

Glittering and gleaming in the sunlight streaming through the window were gold and silver coins, and pieces of eight and any amount of jewel encrusted items.

This unexpected largess was shared out, both Gulliver and Roger Ridout receiving a small share as well as the lesser members of the gang. This was obviously a chest hidden by the Harris family in Elizabethan days when they were pirates long since forgotten.

Within a few days the ship's original cargo of contraband had been swiftly transported across the windswept wastes of Bodmin Moor, on to Bristol, the far north and east of the kingdom.

Luck such as this could not be taken for granted and the risks involved in smuggling were high. A minimum penalty for those caught of transportation to the colonies including Australia was common, and often the penalties were much more severe.

John Knill, the local collector of customs, lived at St Ives Bay where he was Mayor in 1767. He dabbled in smuggling a little himself over the years, embracing Gulliver whenever he should land a cargo on a nearby beach, always turning a blind eye, and receiving a tub or two in return for his loyalty. Local knowledge of safe and secluded routes out of the county were paramount to those in control of transportation, the quick dispatch of these cargoes out of Cornwall was necessary to stay ahead of the Revenue men.

The Gulliver children and descendants

Isaac Gulliver's first borne was Elizabeth, who married William Rolls Fryer. They had 7 children. Gulliver's second daughter Ann married Edmond Wagg in 1796, they had no children. It appears that the marriage between Ann and Edmund Wagg was not a happy one. There were problems from the outset, and less than a year after the wedding her brother (Isaac Gulliver Jr.) helped her leave her home and took her to a place of safety. Edmond Wagg placed an Elopement notice in the local papers.

Elopement notice

Wheras Ann, the wife of Edmund WAGG Esq. of Whitehead Wood near Southampton, did on Sunday night laft, ELOPE from his dwelling house, with her brother, Isaac Gulliver, having taken with her all the Plate and Linen belonging to the said EDMUND WAGG:- THIS is therfore to give Notice, that the faid

Edmund Wagg will not be accountable for any Debts whatsoever his Wife may contract from this day.

Two years later in 1798, Isaac Gulliver Jr died aged 24 years as a result of sleeping on a damp bed while staying at Sherborne. It is probable that he contracted pneumonia, a disease that killed with unfortunate regularity at that time. He had been studying to become an attorney in Wimborne, probably under William Castleman. He undoubtedly also studied smuggling under his father. His body was bought back to Crichel where the family were living at the time, and later interned at Wimborne Minster. The plaque can be found high on the wall next to the beautiful Astronomical clock, opposite to the newly erected tomb stone of his father.

Isaac Gulliver jr   Edmund Wagg
1744-1798   1775-1799

The following year (1799), Ann's husband, Edmund Wagg aged 24 years died. He was interned with his brother in law. Why? We have no idea. He bequeathed everything to his estranged wife Ann. This must have been a deeply distressing time for his mother and father.

Ann Wagg later married Dr Andrew Crawford of Blandford. He died in 1824 aged 61 years. Ann died in 1832, aged 60 years.

The plaque of Isaac Gulliver Jr, & Edmund Wagg in Wimborne Minster

Edward Castleman
1800-1861

Ann Fryer
1799-1883

Ann Crawford
nee Gulliver
1773-1832

Mary E Stephens   Edward Castleman   Fanny M Fuidge
1809-1903   1841-1874   1848-1907

Henry O'H Moore   Mary E Castleman   Henry O'H
1833-1877   1871-1937   Moore
Alice A Fryer   1875-1942
1843-1913

Henry C O'H   Joyce A O'H   Charles A
Moore 1905-1994   Moore   Leavens
L Bruder 1906-1974 1910-2002   1905-1986

The last run

In 1800 Bournemouth consisted of one solitary habitation. This was the house abode of one of the many free traders who infested the Hampshire coast in the exercise of their illicit speculations. The head of the free traders was the renowned Old Gulliver, whose physical strength and daring rendered him a formidable opponent to the 'Philistines' who were stationed in the area for the protection of the revenue.

Fittingly his crowning achievement took place on the beach where Bournemouth pier now stands. Three large luggers, manned by determined crews and deeply laden with silks, brandy, tobacco, and other valuables, successfully ran their respective cargoes.

A convoy of heavily laden horses

An old inhabitant recollects.

That the cortege conveying the contraband inland extended a full two miles in length. At its head rode the old chief mounted on a spirited charger, and doubtless if the 'land–sharks' as they were termed, had dared to interfere with the procession, a bloody encounter would have ensued.

The Reverend Richard Warner noted the following in his Literary Recollections.

Extremely well armed smugglers were capable of challenging and seeing off Customs attacks without much difficulty. As a young schoolboy I witnessed from time to time processions of up to 20 or 30 wagons loaded with kegs of spirits, armed men sitting at the front and rear of each, surrounded by a troop of two or three hundred horsemen, every one carrying on his enormous saddle two to four tubs of spirits, winding deliberately, and with the most picturesque and imposing effort across the heath land on their way towards the wild country to the north of Christchurch.

We must remember that in Gulliver's case, "well armed smugglers" were carrying coshes and black jacks, not pistols.

Thus ended Old Gulliver's smuggling career, he "coiled up his ropes" and anchored on shore where he enjoyed his large fortune. He spent his final years living on the outskirts of Wimborne, where his regular attendance at the Minster soon earned him the position of Church Warden, a post he fulfilled for a good many years. As his health failed he could be seen in his bath chair being pushed around the town by a younger man who had taken on the role of carer and of whom he was very fond.

By 1822 his health was failing so that he took to his bed for several days. Early on the morning of September 13th his wife Elizabeth found him unconscious and by the time the doctor arrived he had passed peacefully away. News of his death spread quickly through the region, from the poorest farm labourer to the wealthiest gentry, for he been known and loved (or at least respected) by all. Although his 'trade' of smuggling was illegal and therefore his employees were also on the wrong side of the law, he was gratefully remembered by the poor, whose lives he had raised from direst poverty. Not only had his contraband enhanced the lives of the nobility, it had, in many cases, enriched them. He gave employment to those that were in desperate need of work, saving many from the bread line over some sixty years. It is also said that whilst he was never afraid to punish betrayal, he had never caused a person's death.

Funeral procession through Wimborne

On the day of his funeral Wimborne was packed with people who came from far and wide to watch the funeral cortege drive to the Minster from his house on the main Cranborne Rd. The funeral carriage, drawn by four elegant black horses with plumes bobbing on their nodding heads, had to force its way through the crowd thronging the town. The Minster was full to overflowing as the heavy coffin - for Gulliver was still a big man - was carefully carried by six pallbearers down the aisle.

After a short service the body of Isaac Gulliver was finally laid to rest next to the Church Warden's seat he had made his own, in the central aisle. It was the family's wishes that the stone covering his tomb was kept simple; only with the words 'Isaac Gulliver 1745-1822' inscribed. The slab, now much worn by decades of passing feet, has recently been moved to the wall of the tower to preserve it, and there is a memorial for his son on the opposite wall.

Isaac Gulliver Burial Certificate

Rumour has it the Minster didn't have to buy Communion wine for a considerable number of years after his death!

In his Will he writes with affection of his two daughters Elizabeth and Ann, bequeathing them £600 and all his chattels. He made several small bequests to friends to his daughter Elizabeth, wife of William Rolls Fryer the banker he left the residue of his extremely large estate consisting of money, farms, properties, Inns, & land.

Part of Gullivers 18 page Will

On her death, Elizabeth in turn passed this fortune to her children and it continues to be passed down through their descendants and we can still trace it through the generations to this day.

Isaac (76) & Elizabeth (72) Gulliver

Banking and the Creation of Bournemouth

In the year 1800 twenty two years before Gullivers death, William Dean, William Castleman and George Adams founded the Christchurch, Wimborne and Ringwood Bank. Perhaps Isaac Gulliver's 'luck of the devil' still held true for his daughter Elizabeth had married William Rolls Fryer, who was a relative of William Castleman. This family tie gave him an important introduction to the Christchurch, Wimborne & Ringwood Bank, as well as the Wimborne bank where he was able to deposit his money at a favourable rate of interest. The bank could then lend his money in the form of mortgages to borrowers wanting to invest in the creation of the town we now know of as Bournemouth. In this way Isaac Gulliver was most definitely involved in financing the initial construction and development of the town.

It is thought that Holdenhurst was the true starting point of the creation of Bournemouth. The Dean family had been yeomen farmers in Holdenhurst for several hundred years and William Dean, The Earl of Malmesbury, Lewis Tregonwell and Sir George Tapps were the founding fathers who quickly purchased land when the Enclosures Act of 1802 came into being.

For decades smugglers, Gulliver amongst them, had built mud houses and cottages in the area; they had inhabited the heathland and shores for a century or more and knew the region like the back of their hands.

They built small shacks and mud walled houses as temporary habitation where they could watch for and await their cargos of contraband to be delivered by sea.

These buildings were scattered about the heath, placed well out of sight of prying eyes, concealed by the large bushes and scrub that grew there. Gulliver also had a building on the uninhabited Sandbanks spit leading to what is now the site of the Studland ferry, which was known as Gulliver's farm.

However historians believe Lewis Tregonwell was the first person to build a respectable brick house overlooking the sea. Tregonwell would also have known the area fairly well as during his army service he had been stationed at Cranborne and his beat would have covered the Bourne heathland as well as the shore line from Poole to Christchurch.

The Christchurch, Wimborne and Ringwood Bank started lending money at about four and a half per cent to those wishing to purchase land, five per cent to farmers, and a rate of about twenty five per cent to smugglers; this higher rate of interest because of the greater risk that they could lose their cargo to the revenue officers. Without doubt the directors of the bank would have been well aware who borrowed money at twenty five per cent and therefore that they were smugglers.

William Dean (of Deans Brewery) acquired the status of gentleman and squire when Little Down fell into his hands by chance from a loan that had been taken out by John Strong, who subsequently became overextended, having borrowed more money from William Dean than he was able to repay.

Unfortunately John Strong died unexpectedly, and, as he had no children, had named two cousins, Mary Hill and Ann Kearly, as his heirs. Ann wanted to sell her half, so, with the property heavily mortgaged, William Dean needed to persuade Mary to sell her share.

Eventually she sold her half to William who thus became the owner of Littledown at a figure considerably below market value.

William Dean had an astute speculating brain and continued to buy land. He acquired 500 acres of the West Cliff and an area that became Dean Park by private treaty for £639. This was the start of the Dean family fortune.

Further awards of the Enclosures Act consisting of 2750 acres were distributed among some 41 people. Almost half of this was acquired by just two men, Sir George Tapps claimed 705 acres and William Dean a further 636 acres, giving Dean a total of 1136 acres. The son of a yeoman farmer, William Deans new status as gentleman land owner was now secure.

In the early 1800's the gentry bought this heathland to add to their farm estates, without any intention to build.

They rented out small holdings to the local farmers at an annual rent. In this way much of the heathland was preserved and therefore ideal for the smugglers to continue their trade.

Business continued to thrive for the Christchurch, Wimborne & Ringwood Bank with Gulliver pouring money into the bank as a safe haven for his money, not only was Isaac protected by his daughter Elizabeth's marriage to William Rolls Fryer, his Grand daughter Ann was now married to Edward Castleman, son of William, also a director of the bank.

Gulliver must have smiled complacently to himself in the knowledge that, having started out as the son of a mere landlord of a country inn, he was now a major investor in a bank. There could be no better place to hide his ill-gotten gains away from the prying eyes of the Revenue. This could have been the beginning of money laundering as we know it.

Late in 1812 William Dean died, last of the male line of the Holdenhurst yeoman farmers. His death was to cause his family much grief over the next generation. In his Will it was clearly stated that the land he had acquired could not be sold for residential building which the other land owners were now starting to do. The trust created left the estates in the hands of two trustees who conscientiously carried out his wishes.

A codicil to his will stated that: "Said testator nominated William Clapcott as his successor in the banking firm of Dean, Castleman & Adams. Giving him all his share capital and interest. This was a double edged sword as the codicil added, *Declaration that all his said estates should be subject to and charged with the payment of all losses which might be incurred in said business. That the said William Clapcott should repay all such with interest as should be occasioned after the Testators death.*"

Perhaps William Dean realised that Clapcott was by nature a gambling man as this codicil made him responsible for not only all his own losses but any the losses the bank might incur as well. William Clapcott accepted the risk not knowing the damage this would cause his wife and son in later years. William Clapcott was head of the bank for six years, during which it began to make heavy losses. William Castleman decided to resign and withdrew his capital. The Bank then changed its name to Dean, Clapcott & Adams.

William Castleman

Now that William Castleman, the bank's only lawyer, was no longer there to give advice, they suffered many financial disasters. Ever the gambler, William Clapcott took this opportunity to play a new and unscrupulous role in the future development of Bourne Mouth.

Desperate for money he took out a private loan from his old friend William Castleman for £2800 at five per cent over sixty years on the property he had inherited from William Dean and in which he and his wife had a life interest. However this amount was not enough to keep the bank afloat and in 1820 a second loan for the sum of £1200 was made to William Clapcott by Castleman on the same terms. Six years later and four years after the death of Isaac Gulliver, Castleman was asked for a further loan of £3900.

William Castleman had, via his wife, inherited a goodly sum from Isaac Gulliver. He was fairly confident that Clapcott would never be able to repay the loans and knew when he defaulted on the payments, the Dean properties which Clapcott had inherited would fall into his hands for a fraction of their original purchase price.

The wily lawyer demanded all the freehold farms and other property as security as well as the income from the residue of his personal estate that had not been invested, plus a 1000 year lease on 50 acres of land awarded under the Enclosures Award to William Dean, for the £3,900 loan being requested. Thus William Castleman invested money from his Gulliver inheritance which helped in the creation of Bourne Mouth. Without a doubt he was a shrewd investor, far sighted and not too afraid of the stigma of being called unscrupulous. William and his wife Mary Clapcott now owed William Castleman the staggering sum of £7,900, some £331,800 in today's terms.

William Clapcott's banking losses continued to mount by the year, in line with other British banks at that time, due to overseas losses and non repayments. In 1827 Clapcott came to William Castleman once again for another loan of £2,500. Now in debt to the sum of £10,400 this final loan gave Castleman even more of a hold over the Dean Estates in Bourne Mouth. Later that year when William Castleman requested repayment of the £10,400 in full, hoping that Clapcott would default on the payment, he was sorely disappointed when William Clapcott managed to pay off the loan in full by borrowing the money from elsewhere so as not to forfeit his estate & properties. However when William

Clapcott died, a mere six years later aged 64, he left his wife Mary and his 21 year old son in serious financial difficulties. In order to pay off William Castleman he had borrowed £13,500 against his estate - enough to pay the debt plus a little extra money to live on.

His son was an introvert and had difficulty communicating with the outside world. On the other hand his wife Mary was an astute woman with financial ideas of her own. Instead of collapsing in despair at this state of affairs, she took control and rearranged her financial affairs. She knew William Rolls Fryer was another direct descendant of Isaac Gulliver and had also benefited from his Will. With land prices rising, Mary Clapcott managed to rearrange the Dean Estate finances with the help of William Rolls Fryer in his role as local banker.

With the arrival of the steam train large numbers of visitors were drawn to this new and exciting watering hole demanding both residential and holiday homes close by the sea with its 'medicinal cures'. Land prices continued to rise apace and new properties and villas were built throughout Bourne Mouth. The unfortunate clause in her late father's Will denied Mary the right to build on the land as Dean thought it would always remain farm land. However in 1839 Mary realised that the 1136 acres of land she owned was worth far more than the £15,000, some £630,000 at today's value, she now owed to William Rolls Fryer. She therefore approached him and asked for 700 acres of the heath land that abutted the sea shore to be returned to her, free of mortgage. It might seem surprising that William Rolls

Fryer agreed to this, duly signing a new agreement releasing 700 acres of land to Mary and her son William.

Nevertheless he did so in the knowledge that the remaining 436 acres of land which was surety against the mortgage he still held, was worth more than the £15,000 she owed him. He had the foresight to realise there was no way she could ever repay him but this ensured he could acquire a large area to the East of Bournemouth which was worth far more than the original outstanding mortgage.

Unusually for the times, Mary Clapcott now became a financial wizard in her own right. She had 700 acres back in her full possession, even though it was heathland and as such not worth a great deal of money. She could see that speculators were willing to pay premium prices further along the coast line for land, so she decided not to sell even though this could have made their current cash starved life easier for both her and her son.

By the early 1850's with a regular rail service in place Bourne Mouth had grown. Shops abounded, hotels were built and a small thriving community flourished. Mary and her son William Clapcott were still living close to or actually on the bread line, but, determined not to sell any land to raise money, they struggled on. They lived in Littledown House which overlooked much of their land; the rents and produce from which as well as interest on the mortgage went to pay off William Rolls Fryer. Some years later, now aged 77, he decided to recall the mortgage so as to settle his estate. He assumed that Mary Clapcott would have to default and the Gulliver money lent to her would bring in a good return if he acquired the land mortgaged to him. Unable to pay,

Mary once again borrowed money from another source and in 1849 she paid Fryer in full. Had her father not written the clause in the Will forbidding any building on the land she would have lived a relatively comfortable life without the need to constantly borrow money.

In 1852 after a long hard debt ridden life Mary died leaving her son William with the financial responsibilities of the estate. In total by now there were 1480 acres, including Littledown House, a total value of £28,600 for probate, with an income of £1,400 which went directly to pay the new mortgagees.

William was an unsophisticated man whose only real interests were farming, livestock and hunting, who thought he would be living on the edge of financial disaster for the foreseeable future.

Since his father had almost bankrupted them his mother had run the financial side of the estates entirely on her own. Without any experience he was now saddled with the £15,000 debts on the new mortgages that had paid off William Rolls Fryer and for which payment had to be met without fail on the days agreed. A mere few days after the death of his mother, the family solicitor arrived at Littledown House. He explained to William that soon after her marriage Mary had taken out a life insurance policy for £2,500. Then some years later when her husband started to borrow larger amounts from William Castleman she had taken out another Life policy against her life with the Equitable Life Assurance Society.

Showing an unusual amount of business acumen, she had never failed to pay her premium on time, even when hardest pressed. Therefore he, William, was now due the total sum, with interest, of £16,500. This put him in a position to pay off the £15,000 and clear his debts in full. For the first time the Dean Estates were now fully owned by William Clapcott junior and all the income from the farms & land was his and his alone. This explains how the money from Gulliver was used to help in the creation of Bourne Mouth, or as we now know it Bournemouth.

During the first few years of the 19th century Sir George Tapps and William Dean started planting Pine trees to beautify the area we know as Talbot Woods.

The first real house that we know of was built in 1810 at the top of the hill overlooking a worthless piece of ground with a stream running into the sea.

Lewis Tragonwell built "The Mansion" with sea views. The building is part of what we know as the Exeter Hotel. The Tregonwells moved in during 1812 and became known as the founders of Bournemouth. But as we know the true founders were the smugglers who had built their small mud houses and rickety shacks throughout Bourn heath for many a long year before the first recognised building was constructed.

Chettle

Once Gulliver's Will had been proved, the money filtered down through his descendants who in most cases put it to good use. One or two managed to squander their share.

Mr Chafin presold Chettle in 1805, as it had been bought from the crown he needed the sovereign's permission to sell the estate which he failed to get.

When Mr Chafin died in 1818 it was found that Chettle was heavily mortgaged to a moneylender in London of the name of Chambers and there was no money to pay off the mortgage. Mr Chambers rode so fast to come to Chettle from London when he heard the news, that his horse dropped dead at the front door. Mr Chafin's illegitimate children thought that they had a case to keep the estate and so it went to court. Chambers went bankrupt and was thrown into Newgate jail. The case proceeded with Chettle being advertised for sale several times over the following years.

Some years later Gregory of Gregory Rowcliff, 1 Bedford Rd, London, solicitor and good friend to Mr Castleman, acted for the Bank of England over the sale of Chettle Estate, Chettle from the Chafin family in about 1845 when Edward Castleman (1800-1861) from Wimborne, bought it. He was married to Anne (1799-1883) a grand daughter of Isaac Gulliver.

Ann went to London to the 1851 Exhibition, where Nelson's ship the Victory was being sold in pieces and bought the deck, which is now the floor of the drawing room.

Henry C ff Castleman (1873-1927), known as Harry was the brother of Edward William Fuidge (1870-1946), and Edith Alice (1868-1957), great, great, grand children of Isaac Gulliver, had inherited a large part of the Kinson area of Bournemouth, which he frittered away over the years.

He trained in Munich, and Paris as a vocalist and later with Dr Huntly of St Peter's, Eaton Square, London.

In 1925 he and his wife Hilda took on a world tour singing and preforming his many songs and plays. In January 1926 he arrived at the Castleman River in Maryland, USA. The drive took them from Philadelphia, to Baltimore, Washington, West Virginia into Ohio, through Kentucky, Tennessee, Georgia, Alabama, Mississippi and into Louisiana with no trouble from the car on their way to San Francisco. From there on to an Asiatic and African tour. Where they visited Japan, China, Burma, India, Palestine, Egypt and on through Europe back to England. Eventually in 1927 on the brink of bankruptcy and in a fit of desperation he committed suicide at his home in Weymouth, he left no children.

1939 Gulliver's money to the rescue

The Castleman family enjoyed living at Chettle for approximately 100 years, bringing up their many children. In 1939 when Edward Castleman, Great, great Grandson of Isaac Gulliver was running the Estate, this changed. Having no children of his own, he invited his elder sister Alice's (Great, great, granddaughter of Gulliver) daughter Esther Bourke, (nee Roe) (thus a Great, great, great, granddaughter to Isaac) to visit him in Chettle and stay for the weekend. Esther had married in India and recently returned to England with her young children but was not yet settled in this country. She duly arrived on 1st September 1939 together with her two children, just two days before the Second World War was declared.

Events leading up to the war had already started with Germany putting troops into Poland and the whole country was in a state of confusion as to what would happen next. On the 3rd September war was declared.

The phone lines were red hot between Chettle and London with Edward and Esther contacting her husband Leslie who had remained in the capital at the war office.

It was decided that Esther and the children should stay in Chettle until things settled down in London and Europe, at which time they could return home to London. Esther, with children Susan, Patrick, and Edward (Teddy), remained in Chettle for the duration of the war; Esther learning about farming and village life at Chettle. In 1944 Edward Castleman became increasingly ill; cancer was diagnosed and after a two year illness he finally died in 1946. As Esther Bourke had been learning the ropes at Chettle and seemed to enjoy the life as did her children, it was decided by the numerous cousins and siblings who were beneficiaries under his Will that Esther should remain in situ and run the estate with her brother Corrie Roe. The major problem they faced after the death of Edward Castleman was a lack of ready money and loans of some £35,000 (approximately £875,000 in today's terms) which had to be paid promptly.

In order to raise money towards the loans and tax it was decided to sell as much furniture, objects d'art, paintings, and farm equipment as was possible.

Shortly before the auction Esther Bourke phoned her cousin Joyce (also a Great, great, great, granddaughter of Gulliver) who had married Charles Leavens, and asked them to attend the auction. On their arrival a covert conversation took place with Esther asking Charles, who had attended many farm sales on his own right, to bid for certain items which Esther wanted to keep but had been forced to put up for auction.

Prices were agreed between Esther & Charles before the auction took place. Charles successfully 'bought in' many items on behalf of Esther, even managing to acquire some at a lower price than was expected, as word had been 'passed around' that some items may not necessarily have been accurately described in the catalogue. It is important to remember this was a remote country house sale held very shortly after the war. The general public were still suffering from the shortages of that war and in the days before television's 'Antiques Roadshow' and similar programmes, were not experts in such matters.

Although the money thus raised went some way towards paying off the loans and capital monies that had to be repaid to a family member who had died some years before, there was still an insurmountable shortfall.

It looked as though the estate could not be saved in its entirety and the option of selling off some parts seemed unavoidable.

After much discussion between various members of the family, one cousin offered to buy the entire estate for himself; his offer was sharply rebuffed. After further long and lengthy debate between Esther Margaret Bourke (nee Roe), Corrie Bernhard Castleman Roe, Elizabeth Alice Roe, children of Edith Alice Castleman who married Bernhard Roe, it was decided to mortgage half the estate not to the banks as this was too risky in case of default.

On the 8th December 1950, the Personal Representatives of Edward William Fuidge Castleman, deceased and their Surety, took out a mortgage to Lt Col Henry Castleman O'Hara Moore OBE, for the freehold lands and premises in the Parishes of Chettle and Tarrant Hinton in the County of Dorset.

The mortgage was between Esther Margaret Bourke, of Chettle House, Chettle, Elizabeth Alice Roe, of 22 Groom Place, London, and Corrie Bernhard Castleman Roe, formally of Groom Place, London, and now of Chettle House, Chettle, Dorset.

The Lender was Lt Col Henry Castleman O'Hara Moore OBE. Of Coolhurst, Lilliput, Poole, Esther's cousin, and brother of Joyce Leavens and thus also a great, great, great, grandson to Gulliver.

Line 4 of the mortgage states: The Lender at the request of the Surety has agreed to lend the said sum to the Executors upon having the repayment thereof with interest thereon secured in manner hereinafter appearing.

Line 5 states: The Executors have not given any assent or made any conveyance in respect of a legal estate in or offering the property hereby mortgaged or any part of it.

It was agreed that Esther Bourke would remain in contact with the lender twice a month to keep him informed of the overall condition of the estate, and or to receive instructions on the running of the estate and village. This was continued after her death by her younger son Edward until 1972, when the mortgage was cancelled, unpaid in full.

The lender was a direct descendant of Isaac Gulliver on both his maternal and paternal sides as his parents were second cousins and great great, grandchildren of Isaac Gulliver. Thus Gulliver's descendants were able to retain and restore Chettle village as a family run estate.

Without the intervention of Henry Castleman O'Hara Moore OBE, some or all of Chettle would most definitely have been divided and parts sold.

Henry O'Hara Moore's generosity was considerable; on the 15 of July 1966 he removed Nursery Cottage, Chettle (now known as The Old Coach House) from the mortgage, giving it to Esther Bourke so that she in turn could present the Cottage to her son Patrick on the occasion of his marriage to Janet Elizabeth Griffiths.

Sadly in 1967 Esther Bourke died aged 63, leaving her children to continue running the estate, under the benevolent guidance of Lt Col O'Hara Moore.

The Sturts of Crichel had known both the Castlemans and the Bourkes for many years as the two estates adjoined each other and made an offer to buy Chettle hoping to increase their land holding in the area.

However the estate was financially secure by this time and their offer was turned down out of hand. Although only the interest on the mortgage had been repaid, and not the original capital investment, Lt Col Henry O'Hara Moore, with his customary foresight and generosity, cancelled the mortgage on the 20 March 1972, as 'paid in full'; just one month before the double wedding of his nephew and niece Beresford O'Hara Leavens and

Monica Helen Leavens, who, as he was childless, were his sole heirs. He did this with the intention of removing any problems for his beneficiaries should he die before the mortgage was cleared.

Chettle estate was thus handed back in full to the Bourke children giving them title to the estate, along with certain agreements as to the future of the village.

Once again it was due to money trickling down through the generations from Isaac Gulliver that Chettle was saved. He could never have realised just what an impact he would have on the people who worked for him, and his descendants.

Appendix

The Bournemouth & Christchurch Inclosure Act 1802 Allotment 44, The Bourn stream was bought by William Driver of Surrey Square, Surrey. The plot was 83 acres & 34 perches.

Plot 44 as bought by private treaty for £262-2s-4d, William Driver appeared to be an early land speculator due to the fact that he sold plot 44 in 1807 to Patrick Crawford Bruce. This was land which ran along the North side of the Bourne stream from Richmond Hill for nearly two miles towards Coy Pond Road. At a later date Driver sold all his other parcels of land which he had obtained in the Inclosure Awards to one P. C. Bruce.

Patrick Crawford Bruce was born in Scotland in 1748 and pursued a successful career as a merchant in Bombay, where he set up the merchant house of Bruce, Fawcett & Co. He returned to England from India in 1794.

In 1822 the land at Bourn stream now known as Bourne Bottom was awarded to Isaac Gulliver; at some later date it is reported that Anne Castleman (1799-1883), laid out the gardens alongside the stream, currently known as Bourn stream in the Winter Gardens more or less as we know them today.

Allendale House, Wimborne.
The architect of Allendale House was Jeffery Wyatt, his uncle was the chief steward for the Anglesey Estate that covered the Sixpenny Handly area. William Castleman

built Allendale House in about 1839, before his death in 1844. William Castleman had his portrait painted by Sir William Beechey (1753-1839), he was appointed portrait painter to Queen Charlotte in 1793. The portrait now hangs on the stairs in Chettle House.

William Bankes of Kingston Lacy, Wimborne, had some 'personal problems' with a young guardsman and had to leave the country in haste for a number of years, he asked Mr Castleman his friend and director of the Ringwood Wimborne and Christchurch bank to assist him.

Mr Castleman used his acquaintance, a solicitor named Gregory of Gregory Rowcliff, 1 Bedford Rd, London to act on his behalf. During Mr Bankes' enforced absence from England, totalling some 15 years, he spent his time collecting artefacts for his house, Kingston Lacy, Wimborne, Dorset, sending them back on a regular basis by ship from around the world to Studland beach which he owned.

Many Wimborne families were very sympathetic to William Bankes, and did not seem to 'outlaw' him as other families had in the county. During his absence from Dorset, William Bankes employed William Castleman solicitor, to assist on the estate, to carry out his instructions, and also to help with the collection from Studland of his boat loads of art and other treasures sent back from Europe. The decendants of Gulliver were obviously very helpful in unloading and supervising the transportation of the artefacts to his house, bearing in mind that the Bankes family had been most accommodating to Gulliver, with regard to Studland and his illegal activities in the past.

During 1854, when William John Bankes realised that he could not openly return to England, it is believed that he made a secret trip from Cherbourg to Kingstone Lacy via Studland, which had been the landing place for so many of his previous shipments. It is thought that later generations of Gulliver would have ensured his safety from arrest, and his safe return from Kingston Lacy to the continent.

Frances and Henry Bankes held an extremely grand ball at Kingston Lacy in 1791, and it is believed that Gulliver and his family would have been invited. The ball is re-enacted at the start and end of each season at Kingston Lacy house. Henry Bankes had been kept well supplied with the import of his favorite drinks at that time.

Kingston Lacy which is now owned by the National Trust along with its extensive gardens and interesting objects d'art is now open to the public.

Chettle House and its village are still owned by the great, great, great, great Grand children of Isaac Gulliver. The family are proud to have retained it through many difficult times, and have slowly modernised the cottages and created The Castleman Restaurant. It is one of the last privately owned family run villages in the country.

ISAAC GULLIVER dates of interest.

1745. Isaac Gulliver is born, Sept 5, at Semington, Wilts.

1758. Isaac Gulliver at Bitmans Chine, March 23.

1768. William Beal Kings Head at Thorney Down.

Isaac Gulliver, Elizabeth Beale at Handley, Oct 3.

Isaac Gulliver living at Blacksmiths Arms, Thorny Down

1770. Elizabeth Gulliver baptised at Handley, Feb 4.

1773. Ann Gulliver is baptised at Handley, April 22.

1775. Owns Pitts Farm, Kinson.

1776. Owns North Eggardon Farm, Dorset

1777. Levi Payne absconds, March 14 with £21. 16s and a nag

Isaac Gulliver of Thorney Down signs mortgage, Dec 27.

1778. Isaac Gulliver, at Kings Arms, Thorney Down. advertises properties, Feb 23

William Beale's stock for sale, 16 June 10.

Volunteers called for at Thorney Down, June 1.

Owns Malt House at Kinson with 75 acres.

Gulliver's House, Corfe Mullen.

1779 Isaac Gulliver's horses sold at Longham, March 29.

Isaac Gulliver living at Longham, December.

1780 Earl of Malmesbury's memoirs.

1782 Isaac Gulliver granted pardon (gen. proclamation dated May 3).

Gulliver stops smuggling tea & spirits but continues with wine.

Gulliver's shop at Kinson to let, Aug 26.

Gulliver announces in the Salisbury Journal his move to Devon.

1783. Isaac Gulliver shown to be a wine merchant, of Kinson, Oct 10.

Iceland's Volcano "Catla" erupts killing 30,000 in Britain

1786. Ann Gulliver of Long Crichel, m. E. Wagg.

1788. Gulliver's house at Kinson, notice to let (tenant Mr.Tait),Feb 11.

Owns Pelhams House, Kinson.

William Beale, bankrupt: Gulliver at Kinson.June 2.

1789. Isaac Gulliver living at Gullivers Farm, West Moors.

Early days of the French Revolution.

1793 Vicomte de Francois-Rene Chateaubriand flees to London.

1796, Living at Long Crichel.

1797. June. Elopement notice served, Ann Wagg (nee Gulliver) leaves her husband Edmund Wagg.

1797 Louis Marquis de Fontanes flees to England with Suard,

1798. Isaac Gulliver junior dies Nov 3,

1799. Edmund Wagg makes Will, February 23

Edmund Wagg dies, March 7.

1807. Gulliver, at Crichel, holds house & land at Kinson. Duke d'Orleans lives in Christchurch as a refugee at Priory House.

1815, Owns Kinson House, Kinson.

1817. Gulliver painted by Thomas Gosse at Wimborne. Living in Wimborne.

1820. Gulliver holding land at Dudsbury.

1822. Gulliver awarded land at Bourne Bottom, and owned or leased 390 acres aprox in Kinson.

Owns High House, Corfe Mullen, Howe Lodge, Kinson.

1821. Gulliver's portrait miniature painted.
1822 Gulliver awarded a grant of land at Bourn Bottom.
Isaac Gulliver dies Sept 13 in Wimborne.
Isaac Gulliver is buried in Wimborne Minster Sept 20.
1830. Elizabeth Gulliver dies in Wimborne on July 18th.
In total at his death he owned land and properties in Dorset, Wiltshire, Hampshire, and Somerset.